»» 目次

*「総語数」 問題文と設問選択肢の合計（概数）

*「難易度」 ★★…易～やや易　★★☆…やや易～標準　★★★…標準～やや難

Training
1

▶ 第１問Ａ形式（情報検索）

目標時間： ６分（挑戦５分）
総語数　： 350 words
難易度　： ★★

You received an email about a conference that you expect to attend next month. 1

（各20点）

From: John Martin <Jmartin@itconf.org> 2

To: All members

Date: July 25, 2019

Subject: Conference in Cardiff

Dear Colleagues, 3

I am writing to tell you about the next Computers in Education conference, which is being held in Cardiff on the 25th and 26th of August. At the conference, there will be presentations on topics ranging from Internet-based learning to the latest educational software for children. And with more presentations than ever before, this year's event promises to be the best yet.

Further information can be found on our website (www.itconf.org). The site 4 also has an online form that you can use to register for the conference. Simply fill out the form, which is the same as the paper-based one used last year, and we will send you the final program by mail, together with a map of the conference area.

Some of you reported problems finding reasonable accommodations at last 5 year's conference. I'm happy to say that the Cardiff Grand Hotel is offering us special low rates this year. Although the hotel is some distance from the conference facility, it is right in the center of the city. The offer is, however, limited to those who make reservations directly with the hotel before August 10th. I look forward to seeing you next month in Cardiff.

John Martin

問 1 John Martin says that this year's conference [1].

① will be open only to those who register by mail
② will have more people attending than ever
③ will have more presentations than previous conferences
④ will include presentations about software made by children

問 2 Visitors to the conference website can [2].

① get in touch with the presenters
② make reservations at the Cardiff Grand Hotel
③ print out a map of the conference area
④ register to attend this year's conference

問 3 John Martin says about the Cardiff Grand Hotel that [3].

① discount reservations can be made at any time
② it is difficult to contact the hotel
③ it is located close to the conference facility
④ its room rates will be cheaper than usual

[1] ① ② ③ ④ [2] ① ② ③ ④ [3] ① ② ③ ④

Class *No.* *Name* 〔得点〕 / 60

Training 2 ▶ 第 1 問 B 形式（情報検索）

目標時間：6 分（挑戦 5 分）
総語数　：330 words
難易度　：★★

You visited your school's website and found the following post. (各20点) 6

The First Annual Speech Contest

7

Students here can now choose to take math, science, history, home economics and PE in English. Next year, we will start several English-only club activities, too. By gathering students from both Japan and other countries who are interested in global education, we can become truly international. Using the theme, 'Join our worlds together', we would like to introduce a speech contest. Current students and past graduates may enter. The event will be broadcast live on our website and the winner's speech will be used in our promotion video and in local TV commercials.

Theme	'Join our worlds together' – how to attract globally minded pupils
Place	School main hall (Map)
Date/Time	March 31st, 2019 11:00-15:30
Timing	Speech ... 10 minutes maximum Q&A ... 5 minutes
Presentation	Slides and images may be used but limited to 8 in total
Application	All entries must be in by March 8th, 2019. Please email a 150-word written or video summary of your speech for selection purposes. All ten final entries will be given a guided tour of global giant ATK Marketing.
Judges	School Principal, Professor Al Brown (International King University), ATK Marketing President Michael Taniguchi
Prizes	First Prize to Third Prize: 25000 yen gift card. The winner will be granted a 5-day summer internship at ATK Marketing.

問 1 The purpose of this post is to find people to help the school [1].

① bring in new applicants
② create bilingual club activities
③ design TV commercial
④ set up an English website

問 2 At the event, the speakers are going to [2].

① design eight different kinds of slides
② hand in a short summary of their speech
③ respond to questions for several minutes
④ watch a video of last year's winner

問 3 The contest may be a useful learning opportunity because the ten entries will [3].

① appear on a television show
② be able to visit an international company
③ learn writing skills from ATK Marketing
④ spend a week doing work experience

[1] ① ② ③ ④　[2] ① ② ③ ④　[3] ① ② ③ ④

Class　*No.*　*Name*　〔得点〕　/ 60

Training
3
▶ 第 2 問 A 形式（情報検索）

目標時間： 6 分（挑戦 5 分）
総語数 ： 490 words
難易度 ： ★★

You are a member of the arts and crafts club at school, and you want to make something popular overseas. On a website, you found a guide for making a craft design that looks interesting. 8

（各12点）

9

Craft Time

Hours of fun all year round. Educational but also lets kids use their imagination and design skills, too.

Ocean in an Egg Box

You will need

A Egg boxes (6 egg size) Blue paint Glitter glue Old newspaper

B Sponge paper (can be bought at arts shops) colored card scissors

C Small shells and stones (adult help needed for small children) jewel stickers tape glue string

Instructions

Step 1: Make A

1. Lay the newspaper on a table to prevent stains and damage.
2. Paint the insides of the egg box. (10 minutes per box)
3. Cover with glitter glue. Dry for 20 minutes.

Step 2: Make B

1. Meanwhile, cut out seaweed shapes from the sponge paper.
2. Draw some fish on the colored card and cut them out.
(Photos of seaweed and fish are fine if you can't draw.) (approx. 5 minutes)

Step 3: Make C adding them to A with B

1. Glue the shells, stones, seaweed shapes and jewel stickers in the box. Warning: Pressing too hard will break the delicate shells.
2. Hang the fish from the top of the box with string for a swimming effect. (approx. 10 minutes)

REVIEW & COMMENTS

Busypapa ***November 18, 2017 at 22:37***

Best thing to do on a rainy day. Fun for all, even my teenage sons loved it! Good as a safe place for my car keys and change.

kinder@garten ***June 4, 2019 14:21***

A big hit with my 1st graders, helped me teach them fish and sea animals. I used blue tissue paper to line the box, it saved time on painting.

問 1 This craft would be good if you want to [1].

① help children think in a creative way

② make something without buying any parts

③ teach people about swimming in oceans

④ use up leftover food in your house

問 2 If you follow the steps, one craft should be finished in around [2].

① 45 minutes ② 85 minutes ③ a few hours ④ half an hour

問 3 Someone who does not have much skill in art would be able to make this craft because [3].

① all parts are sold at art stores

② it can be finished without drawing pictures

③ it is only made in science classes

④ kids can make it alone

問 4 According to the website, one <u>fact</u> (not an opinion) about this craft is that it [4].

① has parts that are easily broken

② is enjoyed most by first grade students

③ is very simple to make

④ should not be used in the rain

問 5 According to the website, one <u>opinion</u> (not a fact) about this craft is that it [5].

① is not just for children to use

② is popular with teenage girls

③ looks better made with tissue paper

④ may damage furniture

[1] ① ② ③ ④ [2] ① ② ③ ④ [3] ① ② ③ ④ [4] ① ② ③ ④
[5] ① ② ③ ④

Class *No.* *Name* 〔得点〕 / 60

Training 4

▶ 第 2 問 B 形式（意見把握）

目標時間： 8 分（挑戦 7 分）
総語数　： 570 words
難易度　： ★★

Your assistant language teacher (ALT) gave you an article to help you prepare for the debate at the end of term. A part of this article with one of the comments is shown below. 10

（各12点）

Uniform Freedom for all ages 11

By Julian Shortland, Virginia Beach
18 JULY 2018 ・11:18 AM

Elementary schools in Petersburg are making school uniforms optional for all grades. This means younger students will now follow the same system already in place in middle and high schools. Since some parents have recently bought new uniforms, children are still free to wear them if they wish. Students will have to follow educational board rules which include no sunglasses or headwear, pajamas, oversized clothes and fashion with bad language or shocking designs.

The change started because of school staff complaints. Teacher Maria Gonzalez said, “We wasted hours scolding them about their uniforms. Besides, they can learn just as well in their own clothes.” She added, “We sent out a questionnaire to parents and 85% of them agreed that uniforms were not necessary.” 12

Despite this, some mothers and fathers have stated, “Not all kids can keep up. Poorer ones may be bullied for being unfashionable. Uniforms help pupils become part of a team.” In addition, a local politician said, “There are security concerns, too. Last winter when a Petersburg student got lost, police soon found him on security cameras as he was wearing a fixed set of clothing and colors.” 13

34 Comments 14

Latest

Marcia Tilsbury 20 July 2018 ・22:46PM
Kids do need to be able to express their characters and clothing is a great way to show their own style. There are plenty of other chances to do this on vacation, weekends and public holidays, though.

問 1 According to the decision explained in the article, all elementary students in Petersburg will now be allowed to [1].

① choose which middle and high schools they want to visit
② design uniforms for all students in the city
③ get their money back after buying uniforms
④ make their own selection about what to wear at school

問 2 Your team will support the debate topic, "We don't need school uniforms." In the article, one opinion (not a fact) helpful to your team is that [2].

① a child can learn the same amount without a uniform
② it takes too much time for the teachers to check all the uniforms
③ only 15% of parents questioned think that uniforms are needed
④ school workers in the USA are not in favor of uniforms

問 3 The other team will oppose the debate topic. In the article, one opinion (not a fact) helpful to that team is that [3].

① children feel that they belong to a group when in uniform
② elementary school students will now follow the same rules as middle and high schoolers
③ local police were able to save a boy thanks to his uniform
④ without a uniform, students may start wearing unsuitable clothes in school

問 4 In the 3rd paragraph of the article, "Not all kids can keep up" means that some students [4].

① are not able to buy the latest trends
② do not have enough space to keep their clothes
③ have to give their clothes to younger family members
④ will grow up faster than other classmates

問 5 According to her comment, Marcia Tilsbury [5] the decision stated in the article.

① has no particular opinion about
② partly agrees with
③ strongly agrees with
④ strongly disagrees with

[1] ①②③④　[2] ①②③④　[3] ①②③④　[4] ①②③④
[5] ①②③④

Class　*No.*　*Name*　〔得点〕　/ 60

Training
5
▶ 第 3 問 A 形式（概要把握）

目標時間： 8 分（挑戦 7 分）
総語数　： 620 words
難易度　： ★★

You are in an English class listening to Mei talk about her experience participating in the welcome party for international center students. 15

（各15点）

> My name is Mei Chen. I'm from Beijing, China. I'd like to talk about the welcome party for the international center students. The party was called for 6 p.m., so I made sure that I was there a few minutes before 6:00. I wore a dress, but most of the students wore casual clothing. Some of them even came in jeans and T-shirts. There were some puzzle games first. After that they served dinner. They had all types of grilled meat and vegetables for dinner. The food didn't have any spices or sauces, so I thought it was all a little too plain. They had some sort of a fruit drink the teachers called "punch" that was pretty good, though. Next, the teachers in charge made a few speeches and then we had some entertainment. Some of the students from Eastern Europe did some folk dancing, which was really nice. A friend from my English class, Antonio, sang and played the drums. After Antonio performed, one of the teachers passed out song sheets. The teacher played the guitar and we all sang the songs. That was a lot of fun. Some of the students went out after the party, but I said I was tired and went back to my room. 16

問 1 Mei enjoyed [1].

① going out with her friends after the party
② listening to Antonio play the drums and guitar
③ the dress-up party for international center students
④ watching the dancers and singing with the teacher

問 2 What did Mei complain about? [2]

① The choice of drink.
② The sing-along songs.
③ The taste of the food.
④ The time the party started.

17 You are in an English class listening to Antonio talk about his experience participating in the welcome party for international center students. (各15点)

18

I'm Antonio Wakabayashi from São Paulo, Brazil. The other night, they had a party to welcome all the new students. I thought it was a little early to start a dinner party at 6:00, so I figured it was okay to be a little late. The food was very nice. They had asked me to sing a few Brazilian songs, so I performed. I sang and played the drums. Most of the other presentations were very interesting. After the student performances, we had a sing-along with Mr. Templeton. He played old favorites on the guitar. That was fun, but I felt disappointed because I suggested some songs and he didn't play them. In the beginning there were only a few people singing, but by the time we finished almost everyone had joined in with us. The party ended at 8:30. Since it was still so early, some of us decided to go out. I invited my friend Mei to go with us, but she said she was too tired. I think she's actually shy and scared to go out with a group. We enjoyed singing so much that we decided to go to a karaoke place so we could keep singing. After that, everyone wanted to go to a pizza shop. I was still kind of full from dinner, but I managed to eat two pieces of pizza.

問1 What did Antonio complain about? [3]

① Not being able to choose the songs.
② Not being able to eat pizza.
③ Not being able to go to karaoke.
④ Not being able to perform.

問2 According to Antonio's speech, which of the following statements is true? [4]

① Antonio didn't seem very interested in the party activities.
② Antonio taught the new students how to play the drums.
③ Antonio tried to make it there before the party started.
④ Antonio thought that Mei was a bit afraid to go out in a group.

[1]	①②③④	[2]	①②③④	[3]	①②③④	[4]	①②③④

Class *No.* *Name* 〔得点〕 /60

目標時間： 6分（挑戦5分）
総語数 ： 360 words
難易度 ： ★★

The following story is about Hideo and his family. (各20点) 19

20 Hideo is a student at a college, studying animals. He hopes to work in a hospital in the future, practicing animal-assisted therapy. He became interested in animal-related jobs because he had often watched his grandfather, Tomozo, happily taking good care of his dog.

21 Tomozo was once hospitalized with a heart attack at the age of 70. After he came home from the hospital, he barely went outside and stopped working in the fields. He spent all day just watching television. His family became increasingly worried about this change. One day Hideo's mother suggested to Tomozo that he keep a dog for company.

22 When the dog came, Tomozo looked very happy. He named the dog Hana. He seemed to enjoy taking care of her every day. There was a gradual change in his complexion. The doctor had said that Tomozo might have another heart attack at any moment, but he seemed to get healthier after Hana arrived. Tomozo spent more time outdoors and he even sometimes did some light work in the fields. She was with him when he read newspapers and listened to the radio.

23 Ten years later, Hana died. Soon after her death, Tomozo passed away at the age of 80. The doctor said that he might not have lived that long without Hana. Hideo also felt that Hana had had a good effect on Tomozo.

問 1 After Tomozo left the hospital, [1].

① he began to work in the fields as hard as before

② he just listened to the radio and read newspapers alone

③ his family was happy to see him staying inside the house

④ he stayed in the house watching television

問 2 After Tomozo got the dog, [2].

① he was hospitalized with another heart attack

② the doctor told him to stay inside with the dog

③ he went outside more often and sometimes even worked in the fields

④ the family asked the experts to give him animal-assisted therapy

問 3 When Tomozo died, [3].

① his dog was no longer alive

② he was as young as 70 years old

③ the family felt sorry for the dog

④ the doctor said nothing about him

[1] ① ② ③ ④　　[2] ① ② ③ ④　　[3] ① ② ③ ④

Class　　*No.*　　*Name*　　〔得点〕　　/ 60

Training 7

▶ 第 4 問形式（図表・長文読解）

目標時間： 8 分（挑戦 7 分）
総 語 数 ： 520 words
難 易 度 ： ★★★

You are in a class, listening to Emma and Jasper give presentations on their joint research. 24

（各20点）

Emma 25

Over the past few decades, travel in Great Britain has become much easier, with faster and more fuel-efficient cars and more convenient public transportation systems. What is more, many households now own two cars. Given this background, one might expect that more people are traveling farther and more frequently. However, according to a survey conducted by the Department for Transport in 2010, people in Britain are traveling less often than before. This trend is true for all modes of transportation, including walking.

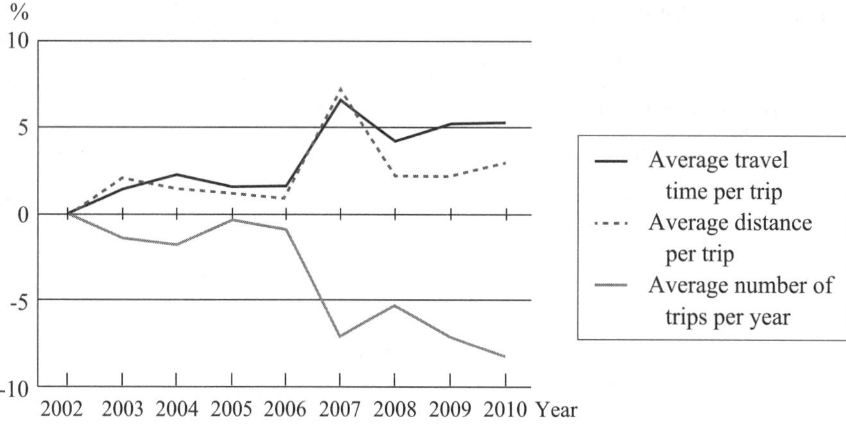

Figure 1. Travel patterns in Britain 2002 - 2010 (percent change).

The number of trips made per person each year did begin to increase in the 1970s but then started to level off in the 1990s. Focusing on the period from 2002 to 2010 (Figure 1), one observes that, while both the averages in travel time and trip distance increased, the average number of trips per person dropped. The average travel time increased by just over 5% from 21.8 minutes in 2002 to 22.9 minutes in 2010, and the average trip distance increased by almost 3% from 6.8 miles to 7.0 miles. On the other hand, the average number of trips fell by approximately 8%. People traveled an average of 1,047 times in 2002, but they made only 960 trips in 2010. 26

27 **Jasper**

What happened in Great Britain to cause this? The decline in the number of trips between 2002 and 2010 can be partly accounted for by falls in shopping and visiting friends at their homes. On average, people made only 193 shopping trips per year in 2010, as opposed to 214 in 2002. Trips to visit friends at private homes declined from 123 to 103 per person per year during this period, whereas the number of trips to meet friends at places other than their homes remained almost constant, at 48 in 2002 and 46 in 2010. The fewer trips for shopping and visiting friends at home may, in turn, be explained by certain changes in society that took place over the period surveyed.

問 1 Based on Figure 1, there was [1].

① a constant decrease in the number of trips made between 2002 and 2010

② a sharp decrease in the distance traveled per trip between 2003 and 2006

③ a similar trend in the travel time and the number of trips after 2007

④ a sudden increase in the travel time and the distance traveled per trip in 2007

問 2 According to Emma, what can we say about the situation in Britain? [2]

① Changes in the public transportation system led to falls in shopping trips.

② From 2003, the average travel time was always more than 21.8 minutes.

③ More people are traveling farther and more frequently today than before.

④ People in Britain walk more frequently now compared to several decades ago.

問 3 The main point of Emma and Jasper's presentations is that [3].

① people find traveling in Britain more convenient than before

② people in Britain traveled more often in the 1990s than in the 1970s

③ the number of cars in each British household has increased

④ there is a trend among people in Britain to travel less frequently

[1] ①②③④　[2] ①②③④　[3] ①②③④

Class　*No.*　*Name*　〔得点〕　/ 60

目標時間： 11 分（挑戦 9 分）
総語数 ： 600 words
難易度 ： ★★☆

You read a story and made notes about it. （各15点） 28

One of the most remarkable stories I know is about a man called Robertson McQuilkin. As a young man, he dreamed of becoming the president of Columbia Bible College in Columbia, South Carolina. He looked up to his father, who had held this position, and he hoped to take his father's place someday. 29

Robertson McQuilkin's dream came true. One day he did become the president of Columbia Bible College. When he became the president, he was convinced that he was called by God and was worthy of that position. 30

He worked as president of that college for a number of years, and he did very well and was respected and loved by many people. 31

Then one day Dr. McQuilkin realized he had a tragedy on his hands. His wife began to show the symptoms of Alzheimer's disease. She became worse in a short time, and in a few months she was in terrible condition. She not only lost her memory of much of their life together, but she was unable to even recognize him. She lost all awareness that he was her husband. 32

Robertson McQuilkin made his decision. He resigned the presidency of the college so he could give full-time care to his wife. Without question, he chose not his job, but his love for her. 33

There were some realists who told him there was no meaning in what he was doing. Anybody could take care of his poor wife, they told him, but not anybody could be president of the college. And after all, she didn't even recognize him when he came in the room to help her. 34

Then there were some religious people who said he was walking away from what God called him to do. He should carry out his social responsibility, which was more important, they said. 35

The man's answers were amazing. To the realists he admitted that his wife didn't know who he was. But that wasn't important, he told them. "The really important thing was that I still knew who she was, and that I saw in her the same lovely woman I had married decades ago," he said. 36

37 Then he turned to the religious people. His words to them were even more profound: "There is only one thing more important than your job" he told them. "And that is a promise. And I promised to be there for her 'until death do us part.' "

Your notes:

About a man named Robertson McQuilkin

■ <u>In his younger days</u>

・Robertson McQuilkin [1].

■ <u>An important event</u>

・Robertson McQuilkin quit his job because [2].

→ Some realists thought ... : [3]

■ <u>Dr. McQuilkin's thoughts in the latter part of the story</u>

・[4]

問 1 Choose the best option for [1].

① did not like his father who was the president of the college

② did not want to become the president of the college after all

③ had a dream that he would resign at an early age and his dream came true

④ was successful in realizing his dream of becoming the president of the college

問 2 Choose the best option for [2].

① he became seriously ill

② he wanted to take care of his wife

③ some people said he was not responsible

④ there was something wrong with his hand

問 3 Choose the best option for [3].

① He should ask someone to look after his wife.

② It was an admirable act that he did for love.

③ Some religious people would admire his decision.

④ Someone else would make a good president of the college.

問 4 Choose the best option for [4].

① He believed that his wife would eventually recognize him.

② He thanked some religious people for agreeing with his decision.

③ He wanted to let the people around him know that he had not changed his mind.

④ He was surprised that his wife remembered the promise he had made.

[1] ① ② ③ ④ [2] ① ② ③ ④ [3] ① ② ③ ④ [4] ① ② ③ ④

Class *No.* *Name* 〔得点〕 / 60

MEMO

Training 9

▶ 第 6 問 A 形式（長文読解・情報整理）

目標時間： 9 分（挑戦 7 分）
総語数 ： 610 words
難易度 ： ★★☆

You are learning about sports science at school and preparing to give a presentation in class. You have found the article below and made notes about it. 38

（各15点）

In 1996, 200 million Americans watched the Summer Olympics in Atlanta on television. Televised sports are so popular that they have created highly successful, all-sports television networks. In addition, they have led to an adult fitness boom, which has flourished as more and more people are exercising to keep themselves healthy and youthful. And today's American heroes are not politicians, business executives, or scientists. 39

How did sports become such an important aspect of American life? Let's start with the definition of "athlete." Baseball players and marathon runners are athletes, but chess and bridge players are not. This is because sports in modern society are competitive, rule-based activities that require physical skills. Athletes compete against themselves, another individual, an established record, or other teams. They may be amateurs who play purely for enjoyment, or they may be professional athletes who are paid for their efforts and display their skills before a paying audience. 40

American sports history examines the development over time of athletic activities, particularly the emergence of specific sports which have their own rules and institutions. Why, for example, are there eleven players on a football team? The study of sports also analyzes the relationships between sports and social institutions, political and economic structures, geography, and group and individual behavior. For instance, why is baseball considered the national sport? How did American society shape the development of sports? How did the loss of public space influence the rise of sports? Finally, the study of sports also involves considering how sports have influenced American values and social behavior. 41

Until recently, historians rarely studied sports because it seemed trivial, or because they considered other topics to be more important. Furthermore, 42 historians who wanted to study sports were often afraid that they could never get a job if they wrote research papers on sports. Even noted historians who wanted to study sports were worried that writing about it would mark them as researchers of an unimportant subject.

43 Academic interest in sports history emerged in the early 1970s, encouraged by historians who began to realize that the study of sports explained certain central themes of American history, particularly class, race, and gender issues. Many realized that analyzing the myths, realities, symbols, and customs in sports provided an excellent means for examining and understanding American values and beliefs. Today, sports history has expanded into a popular area of study, and it is no longer simply social history, but may also be economic history, urban history, political history, educational history, or cultural history, depending on the topics and questions under consideration.

NOTES

Paragraph 1: The popularity of televised sports has [1].

Paragraph 2: An athlete is basically defined by [2].

Paragraph 3: The study of American sports history clearly shows [3].

Paragraph 4: In the past, the study of sports was [4].

問 1 Choose the best option for [1].

① caused the Summer Olympics in Atlanta

② created fewer American heroes than before

③ made many Americans become more physically active

④ resulted in fewer all-sports channels on television

問 2 Choose the best option for [2].

① how he or she competes physically

② how much he or she is paid to perform

③ how popular he or she is in a particular sport

④ how successful his or her team is in sports

問 3 Choose the best option for [3].

① how American values have shaped public spaces

② how geography relates to group and individual behavior

③ that baseball has no social institutions

④ that there is a relationship between sports and society

問 4 Choose the best option for [4].

① considered an easy way to write a research paper

② looked down upon by most scholars and historians

③ seen as something only specialists could understand

④ viewed as a very profitable experience

[1] ① ② ③ ④　[2] ① ② ③ ④　[3] ① ② ③ ④　[4] ① ② ③ ④

Class　*No.*　*Name*　〔得点〕　/ 60

MEMO

目標時間： 11 分（挑戦 9 分）
総語数 ： 640 words
難易度 ： ★★☆

44 You are preparing a presentation on renewable energy. You are going to read the following magazine article to understand the state of wind power. （各15点、問2は完答）

45 Wind is an increasingly valuable source of energy — helping to bring electricity into our lives. At the National Wind Technology Center (NWTC) in Colorado, scientists are working to improve wind-power technology and lower the cost of generating electricity. Generating power from the wind leaves no harmful waste products behind, says NWTC's Jim Johnson. Best of all, the supply is unlimited. "The wind is always blowing somewhere," says Johnson.

46 The potential for wind power is huge. But right now, the United States gets less than one tenth of a percent of its electricity from wind energy, Johnson says. Some experts say it's possible to increase that number to 20 percent or more. In theory, North Dakota alone could supply one third of the country's energy if there were an efficient way to transport the energy to where it's needed. The U.S. Department of Energy estimates that the world's winds could generate 15 times the amount of energy now used around the globe, if only we could make good use of them.

47 Even so, there are some people who argue that wind energy production is far from perfect. One of the biggest problems with wind is its unreliability. Though the wind might always be blowing somewhere at any time, there's no guarantee that it will blow all the time at any particular place.

48 The faster and more often the wind blows, the cheaper and easier it is to get power from it. So wind farms tend to be built in the windiest places, such as Minnesota and Kansas. Unfortunately, these places are far from cities on the coast, where a large number of people live. There's still no good way to transport wind energy over long distances.

49 In addition, wind power plants are also thought to affect human health because the turbines create low-frequency sounds and other noise problems. There are also issues with **durability**, as there have been reports of large wind turbines falling down. These problems lead many to believe that wind power plants cannot

be built in urban areas.

50 There's still a lot of research to be done on making sure that wind power does its job efficiently, safely and cheaply. However, wind power has the potential to make the world less dependent on coal and oil, and to help clean up the environment.

Wind Power as an Energy Source

■ About wind power

- According to Jim Johnson of the NWTC, the best thing about wind power is that [1].

■ Problems with Wind Power

Characteristics of wind	・[2]
Locations of power plants	・[3]
Health problems	・[4]
Safety problems	・There is danger of wind turbines falling.

問 1 Choose the best statement to complete the note. [1]

① the supply of wind power is endless

② wind power is more efficient for its low cost

③ wind power is widely used in the U.S.

④ wind-power technology is well developed throughout the world

問 2 Put the options into the boxes [2] ～ [4] to complete the note.

① The wind does not always blow in the same place.

② People have to move closer to a power plant.

③ People may be bothered by the noise from wind power.

④ There is no good way to transport wind energy.

問3 According to the article, which of the following statements is true? [5]

① Currently, North Dakota alone produces one-third of the energy used in the U.S.

② It is estimated that wind could produce more energy than is currently used around the world.

③ More than 10 percent of the electricity now used in the U.S. comes from wind energy.

④ The U.S. gets more than one-fifth of its electricity from wind power.

問4 The word **durability** in the fifth paragraph is closest in meaning to [6].

① condition of the human body and mind

② state of the weather

③ the ability to last long

④ the ability to produce

1	①②③④	2	①②③④	3	①②③④	4	①②③④
5	①②③④	6	①②③④				

Class　　No.　　Name　　〔得点〕　　/ 60

MEMO

Training
11
▶ 第 1 問 A 形式（情報検索）

目標時間： 6 分（挑戦 5 分）
総語数 ： 350 words
難易度 ： ★★☆

The following texts are emails exchanged between John and Maria. （各30点） 51

52

Hi Maria!

When we go shopping the day after tomorrow, why don't we meet in front of the department store at 4:00 P.M.? The websites say that the department store and the shopping mall are both open on the day, but should we check out the department store first? They have a wider selection of things we could buy for Mom, and their restaurants are better. They have a really good Italian restaurant, so the three of us should eat dinner there. The bus I'm taking is scheduled to arrive just before 4:00. I don't think there will be much traffic, so I'm pretty sure I'll be there on time, but there's a chance I may be a little late. Talk to Kate about it, and if there are any problems get in touch with me. Looking forward to seeing you!

John

53

Hi John!

Kate and I are both OK with that time, and Kate said that she will take the train that arrives about ten minutes before 4:00. I think we should go to the department store, too. She and I were talking about buying Mom a sweater she saw in the department store. Mom really likes that shop — but it's a little expensive, so let's go there first and check it out. The Italian restaurant also sounds great! I haven't had Italian food in a long time. I'll go a little bit early and buy Mom a birthday card at the stationery shop in the shopping mall.

See you the day after tomorrow!

Maria

問 1 John is not certain about [1].

① whether or not the shopping mall will be open the day after tomorrow

② whether or not there is an Italian restaurant in the department store

③ whether or not his bus will arrive on time

④ who should tell Kate the plans for the day

問 2 Maria probably thinks that the department store is a good place to shop because of [2].

① its distance from the station

② her mother's favorite shop

③ a restaurant she has always wanted to visit

④ a shop that sells birthday cards

[1] ① ② ③ ④　　[2] ① ② ③ ④

Class　　*No.*　　*Name*　　〔得点〕　　/ 60

目標時間： 6 分（挑戦 5 分）
総語数 ： 470 words
難易度 ： ★★☆

You are planning to travel to New York. You found a website for a hotel. （各20点） 54

55

Riverside Hotel

234 W 61st St. New York, NY 10032
Book online or call **0044-33-229938**

The Riverside Hotel is located on the Upper West Side of New York, NY, and welcomes tourists and business people visiting the city. The hotel is one block away from the Museum of Natural History. Times Square is ten blocks from the hotel. Lincoln Center and Central Park are five blocks away. The front desk is available 24 hours a day and offers tour assistance.

Nightly Room Rates

Standard single room including breakfast : $98.00
Standard twin room including breakfast : $148.00
Check-in time — 3 pm Check-out time — 12 pm
Photo identification required upon check-in
No pets allowed

Driving Directions

From JFK International Airport : (Approximate distance to the hotel is 20 miles.)

- Take the Belt Parkway west to the Brooklyn Battery Tunnel.
- Take the West Side Highway north. Exit at 72nd St.
- At the second traffic light, turn right on 71st St. and go down to 61st St.
- The hotel is located on the left.

Parking

Why worry about your vehicle or struggle to find a convenient parking space in New York? Take advantage of our convenient parking, which is located across the street from Grand Central Terminal, giving you easy access to trains, subway lines and the entire city. Don't worry about your vehicle or rental car — our hotel parking is safe and secure, so you'll never waste time trying to locate your parking spot.

Parking cost : $20.00 per day
If the vehicle requires two spaces, the guest will be charged for two cars.

Area Activities

Broadway ..... 2 blocks
Times Square ..... 10 blocks
Bronx Zoo ..... 8.0 miles
Central Park ..... 5 blocks
Lincoln Center ..... 5 blocks
Statue of Liberty ..... 1.5 miles

問 1 Which of the following is true regarding the location of the hotel? [1]

① The hotel is located in a quiet, suburban area of New York City.
② The hotel is within walking distance of an international airport.
③ There are many farms and wineries near the hotel.
④ The hotel is located in town near a lot of tourist spots.

問 2 Which of the following documents can be presented in order to identify yourself when you check in? [2]

① student ID without photo
② round trip air ticket
③ valid passport
④ hotel reservation coupon

問 3 Which of the following is true according to the description of the hotel? [3]

① The rate for a standard twin room is more than twice as expensive as that of a standard single room.
② You can bring your dog and let it stay in your room.
③ The hotel makes a point of how convenient its parking lot is.
④ Visitors to the hotel are encouraged to use the train or subway.

[1] ① ② ③ ④　　[2] ① ② ③ ④　　[3] ① ② ③ ④

Class　　*No.*　　*Name*　　〔得点〕　　/ 60

目標時間： 7分（挑戦6分）
総語数 ： 460 words
難易度 ： ★★☆

You are thinking of making a snack this weekend. On a website, you found a recipe that looks good. 56

（各12点）

57

My Favorite Recipes.com

Search My Favorite Recipes.com [ ] [Search]

Recipes | Cooking Tips | Measurements | Comments | Shop

Banana muffins

POSTED BY: Kim

SERVINGS: 12 muffins

INGREDIENTS:

3 bananas, mashed	1/2 cup brown sugar	1/2 cup chopped walnuts
1/4 teaspoon salt	2 cups all-purpose flour	1 teaspoon vanilla
1/2 cup butter, softened	1 teaspoon baking powder	
1/4 cup milk	1 teaspoon baking soda	2 large eggs

DIRECTIONS:

1. Preheat oven to 375 degrees F (190 degrees C).
2. In your mixing bowl, mix together butter and brown sugar until the mixture is creamy. Add bananas, milk, eggs and vanilla, mixing well. Gently stir in flour, baking powder, soda and salt, until moistened. Add the walnuts. Pour the mixture into a muffin pan.
3. Bake at 375 degrees F for around 20 minutes, until a toothpick inserted into a muffin is dry when it comes out. Allow to cool in the pan for 5 minutes. Then place the muffins on a wire rack to finish cooling.

COMMENT ON / RATE THIS RECIPE

58

COMMENTS:

★★★★☆

I wanted lower calorie banana muffins so I combined this recipe with my favorite low-fat muffin recipe. I used 1/4 cup of unsweetened applesauce instead of the butter, used only 1 egg, and only half the sugar (1/4 cup). The applesauce not only lowers the calories, it also makes the muffins taste even better.

Janet in Oklahoma

MORE COMMENTS...

問 1 When you follow Kim's recipe, one of the things you should put into the mixing bowl first is [1].

① bananas　② eggs　③ flour　④ sugar

問 2 According to Kim's recipe, you [2].

① can take the muffins out of the pan as soon as they are cooked
② should be warming up the oven while you are mixing the ingredients
③ should mix the flour, baking powder, soda and salt until it is creamy
④ will need two mixing bowls and more than three teaspoons

問 3 According to the website, if you do not have butter, you can still make the muffins [3].

① if you add one more egg
② if you follow Kim's recipe
③ if you use different ingredients
④ without changing the amount of the other ingredients

問 4 According to the website, one fact (not an opinion) about this recipe is that [4].

① a toothpick is inserted into a muffin to make it easier to eat
② it is for people who are too busy to spend a lot of time cooking
③ low-fat muffins are popular
④ the muffins must be left for more than 5 minutes after baking before eating them

問 5 According to the website, one opinion (not a fact) about this recipe is that Janet's muffins [5] Kim's.

① are easier to make than
② are more delicious than
③ have more calories than
④ have the same ingredients as

[1] ① ② ③ ④　[2] ① ② ③ ④　[3] ① ② ③ ④　[4] ① ② ③ ④
[5] ① ② ③ ④

Class　*No.*　*Name*　〔得点〕　/ 60

Training
14

▶ 第 2 問 B 形式（意見把握）

目標時間： 9 分（挑戦 7 分）
総語数 ： 660 words
難易度 ： ★★☆

Your teacher showed you a school website to help you prepare for the debate in the next class. A part of this website with one of the comments is shown below. 59 （各12点）

Changes in School Rules 60

The school officials are considering allowing students to ride motorbikes or scooters to school. Some parents approve of this plan, while others are opposed. Ms. Singh, whose son is in the eleventh grade, made the following statement:

"I would be very concerned for my son's safety if students were allowed to ride motorbikes to school. First, there isn't enough space at school to park them. Second, motorbikes are expensive to buy and maintain. And most of all, they're dangerous. High school students are not ready to ride such risky machines. Have you ever seen how carelessly they act when they ride their bicycles? They use their cell phones, eat and drink, and even read books, all while flying through the streets. They're much too irresponsible. With a motorbike, they could really cause damage for themselves or someone else." 61

Mr. Hutchins, the father of a twelfth-grader, said the following: 62

"I understand the worries that many parents have about safety. However, for families like ours that live far away from school, life would be much more convenient if students could ride motorbikes. My wife and I both have full-time jobs, so we're much too busy to drive our daughter to school. We practiced many hours with her, so we have no doubt that she is very careful when she rides. My proposal is that students be given a basic test concerning the rules of the road. Only if they pass, they can ride their motorbikes. If not, they have to start over from scratch."

34 Comments 63

Latest

Ms. Yang, the mother of an 11th-grade student 20 July 2018 ・22:46PM

I'm not sure how we can solve the problem of parking space, but I think students should be allowed to ride motorbikes to school with certain conditions. My daughter is on the basketball team, and she gets home from school late every day. There usually aren't any other people walking in our neighborhood, and I worry that it's too dangerous for her to walk home on the dark street from the bus stop. Why don't we let students ride motorbikes to school only if they have permission from their parent or guardian, and their homeroom teacher or the teacher responsible for their extracurricular activity?

問 1 According to this website, there is a possibility that [1] will increase if the school's plan is approved.

① dangers on dark roads
② the risk of accidents
③ time it takes to get to school
④ time spent by parents taking children to school

問 2 Your team will oppose the debate topic, 'Students should be allowed to ride motorbikes or scooters'. In this website, one opinion (not a fact) helpful for your team is that [2] .

① high school students have not shown the level of responsibility needed to ride motorbikes.
② students need safety lessons before getting permission to ride motorbikes.
③ there are too many accidents involving students, so bicycles should also be banned.
④ we have to get enough parking space for students as soon as possible.

問 3 The other team will support the debate topic. In this website, one opinion (not a fact) helpful for that team is that [3] .

① parents worry too much about safety, and this is unfair to responsible students
② permission to ride motorbikes should be granted to students who live far from school
③ students who show knowledge of traffic rules should be allowed to ride motorbikes
④ young people will learn about road safety if they start riding motorbikes early

問 4 In Ms. Yang's comment, she talks about [4].

① conditions for allowing students to ride motorbikes

② keeping children from riding on dangerous roads

③ reviewing time spent in extracurricular activities

④ ways to find more parking space

問 5 In her comment, Ms. Yang says that she [5] the plan to change the school rules.

① agrees with

② has no particular opinion about

③ partly disagrees with

④ strongly disagrees with

[1] ① ② ③ ④　[2] ① ② ③ ④　[3] ① ② ③ ④　[4] ① ② ③ ④

[5] ① ② ③ ④

Class　*No.*　*Name*　〔得点〕　/ 60

MEMO

Training

15

▶ 第３問Ａ形式（図表・長文読解）

目標時間： 7分（挑戦６分）
総語数 ： 410 words
難易度 ： ★★☆

You are interested in international volunteer activities. You are going to read the following article to understand what JOCV is. 64

（各20点）

JOCV (Japan Overseas Cooperation Volunteers) is a program that sends young people (age 20-39) overseas as volunteers. It started in 1966. Since then, more than 45,000 people have been sent to about 90 countries, where people suffer from poverty, hunger, diseases, poor education and many other problems. The number of volunteers increased from about 111 in 1966 to about 1,800 in 2019. 65

What kinds of work are the volunteers engaged in? The volunteers were divided into seven work fields in 1966. Almost half of the volunteers worked in only one of the seven fields, *Agriculture, Forestry and Fisheries. In the second place was Civil Engineering, and in the third was Maintenance. However, the situation has changed in the last 50 years. In 2019, the largest number of volunteers worked in the field of Education and Culture. The second place was taken by *Health and Hygiene, followed by Social Welfare. 66

There are various activities in each field, and they have been expanding in a variety of ways. For example, activities related to HIV/AIDS awareness, which did not exist 50 years ago, are now a *crucial part of Health and Hygiene. As for Education and Culture, science and math teachers are badly needed. In some countries you can be a science or math teacher without a teacher's qualification. The participants are not limited only to experts such as nurses or car mechanics. At JOCV young people get opportunities to make good use of their hobbies or interests to help promote world peace and friendship. 67

* Agriculture, Forestry and Fisheries「農林・水産」 Health and Hygiene「保健衛生」 crucial「重要な」

問 1 Out of the following four pie charts, which illustrates JOCV's fields of works in 2019? [1]

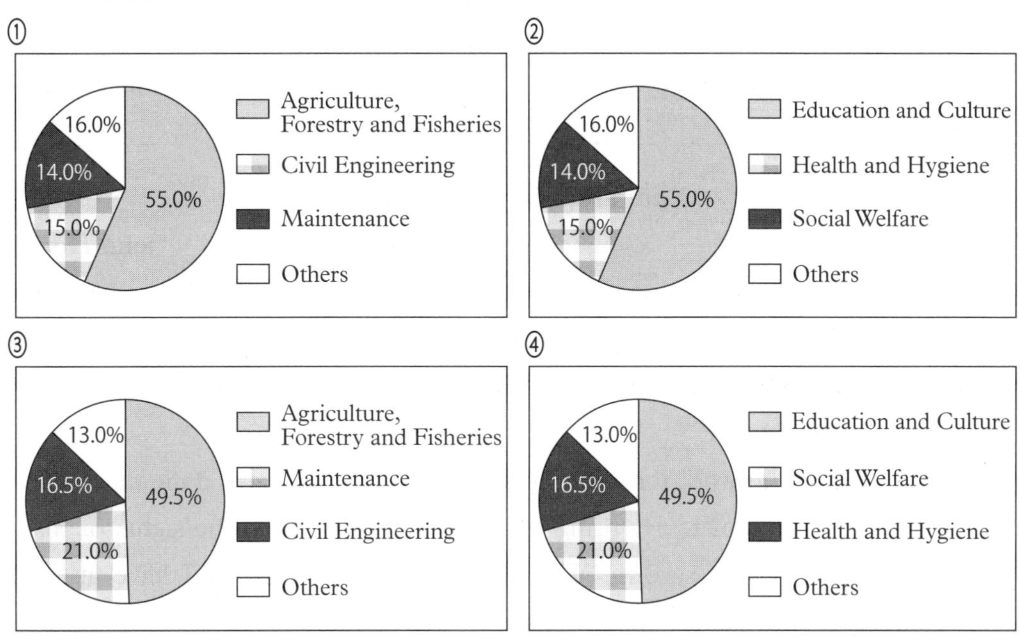

問 2 According to the passage, JOCV [2].

① is a volunteer group that helps young people study abroad
② encourages young people to engage in volunteer activities overseas
③ has sent a lot of young volunteers to about 20 countries
④ is an organization that helps developing countries get richer

問 3 According to the passage, [3].

① in 1966, more volunteers worked in Agriculture, Forestry and Fisheries than in Education and Culture
② nowadays only experts can join JOCV
③ science teachers are needed, but math teachers are not
④ activities to raise HIV/AIDS awareness have been important since the start of JOCV

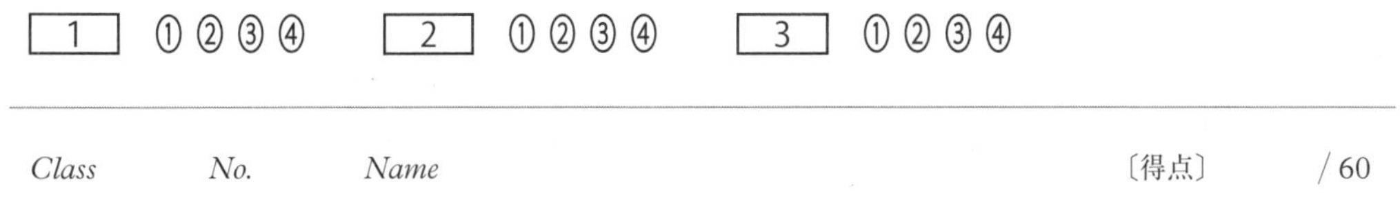

Class *No.* *Name* 〔得点〕 / 60

目標時間： 8 分（挑戦 7 分）
総語数 ： 510 words
難易度 ： ★★☆

You are talking about a story in a class. （各20点、問1は完答）  68

Real and Virtual Experience

69

John Horton

When I was a college student, I did a lot of traveling abroad. That was because a professor encouraged me to do so. She said, "Now is the time for you to travel around the world, expand your knowledge through actual experiences and have fun!" I agreed with her.

Since I started to work for a food company, however, I have done most of my traveling via the Internet. By using the Internet, I have seen the sights of many cities on my computer screen. With the help of the Internet, I have also got information about food in different countries. 70

In this way, I was beginning to feel that actual trips were no longer necessary, when I happened to read a famous chef's comment on the Internet. He said, "It is very difficult to have real Italian food in a foreign country, because we eat food and the air around us at the same time. So why don't you fly over to Italy and enjoy real Italian dishes?" 71

Those words reminded me of my professor's advice. As information technology advances, you might be able to do without making some real trips. But this also means that you will miss the various pleasures you can get from traveling. 72

Today there are people who avoid direct contact with others and spend much of their time on the Internet. It is not surprising to see a group of people talking not with each other but into their cellular phone. It seems as if such people are surrounded by an invisible wall. They seem to be losing out on a good chance to meet and talk with other people. 73

I do not think that they are taking good advantage of information technology. We should use information technology as a tool to make our daily communication more fruitful. However, we should never let it reduce our time for face-to-face communication. Let's make use of information technology more wisely, and have great fun in experiencing the actual world. 74

問 1　Put the following events (①～④) into the order in which they happened.

[1] → [2] → [3] → [4]

① He experienced many real trips.

② He read a comment on the Internet.

③ He recalled the recommendations from his professor.

④ He took virtual trips instead of going to places.

問 2　A famous chef's comment made him realize [5].

① that there was a limit to what the Internet could offer

② that he did not have to go to Italy to taste real Italian food

③ that trips on the Internet were better than real ones

④ that he should enjoy surfing on the Internet much more

問 3　He is worried [6].

① that the increase of cellular phones might cause a problem on the Internet

② that invisible walls might make our face-to-face communication fruitful

③ that those who cannot use cellular phones or the Internet might feel left behind and lonely

④ that too much use of information technology might decrease our time for direct communication

[1]	① ② ③ ④	[2]	① ② ③ ④	[3]	① ② ③ ④	[4]	① ② ③ ④
[5]	① ② ③ ④	[6]	① ② ③ ④				

Class　　*No.*　　*Name*　　〔得点〕　　/ 60

目標時間： 11 分（挑戦 9 分）
総語数 ： 630 words
難易度 ： ★★★

Your teacher is telling your class about students who studied abroad, and your class is going to give their opinions. The first to present is Sarah. 75

（各15点）

Teacher : Study-abroad programs have become increasingly popular among American students. Since the 1980s, many American universities have expanded their study-abroad programs, aiming to increase the number of students who take part in them. The number of American students studying overseas increased slowly at first. Then, in the first decade of the 21st century, it rose by nearly 80%. Europe was the most popular destination, followed by Latin America and Asia. A study was carried out to identify the factors which influenced students' decisions to study abroad. 76

The study involved 231 university students who had studied abroad. They responded to an online survey, which consisted of questions related to the organization of the programs (Program-related Factors) and about students' anticipated experiences while overseas (Experience-related Factors). 77

Table 1 shows the top five Program-related Factors affecting the decisions to study abroad, and the percentages of the participants who placed importance on those factors. The impact that studying abroad would have on the participants' career prospects topped the list. Next, the participants showed concern over whether the study-abroad programs would affect the time when they graduated. This was followed by consideration of how long they would spend abroad. As for the other factors, slightly greater importance was placed on the costs of the programs than on the academic assistance they would receive while abroad. 78

Table 1 *Top Five Program-related Factors*

Factor	Percentage of participants choosing important
Impact on career prospects	91%
(A)	84%
(B)	80%
(C)	74%
(D)	71%

79 The researchers also examined Experience-related Factors. As Table 2 shows, and as has been seen in other earlier studies, the three leading factors were related to culture, independence, and travel opportunities. Learning how to communicate with people from other cultures and visiting historical sites were also regarded as major factors. The authors of this study had expected that opportunities to learn foreign languages would strongly influence the students' decisions to study abroad. However, less than 40% of the participants mentioned this as a factor.

Table 2 *Top Five Experience-related Factors*

Factor	Percentage of participants choosing important
Learning about other cultures	96%
Learning to be independent	94%
Opportunities to travel	92%
Improving communication skills	88%
Access to historical sites	78%

80 **Sarah :** There are increasing demands in the business world for employees who have studied overseas. Therefore, the findings of this study are useful for universities seeking to improve their students' employment prospects. Likewise, there would be benefits in investigating how the experience of studying abroad influenced what the participants did after returning home.

問 1 According to the teacher, which of the following is true about American universities' study-abroad programs? [1]

① A reduction in the number of students studying abroad was seen after the year 2000.

② Latin America was the top destination for students studying abroad in 1980.

③ More students studied abroad after universities offered additional overseas opportunities.

④ The rate of increase in the number of students studying abroad was stable throughout the study.

問 2 In Table 1, which of the following does (C) refer to? [2]

① Length of program
② Possibility of graduating on time
③ Program expenses
④ Study guidance

問 3 The teacher mentions that [3] .

① learning foreign languages was more influential to students than learning about how to be more independent
② more students showed interest in going to historically important places than in learning foreign languages
③ previous studies found that learning foreign languages was more important than learning about other cultures
④ the authors were surprised that learning foreign languages ranked higher than cultural factors for the students

問 4 Sarah mentions that [4] .
① it may be valuable to know the outcomes of studying overseas
② more universities make lists of prospective students who have studied abroad
③ sending university students abroad could be a business opportunity for companies
④ there are many reviews of similar studies on how many students studied abroad

[1] ①②③④　[2] ①②③④　[3] ①②③④　[4] ①②③④

Class　*No.*　*Name*　〔得点〕　/ 60

MEMO

Training

18

▶ 第 5 問形式（長文読解・情報整理）

目標時間： 16 分（挑戦 14 分）
総語数 ： 820 words
難易度 ： ★★★

You read a story and made notes about it. （各12点） 81

In 1949, my parents made the big move from Elmira, New York to Colorado, along with three very tiny children and all their household possessions. My mother had carefully wrapped and packed many precious family treasures, including four boxes of her mother's hand-painted dinner set. Grandmother had painted this lovely set herself, with a pattern of forget-me-not flowers. 82

Unfortunately, something happened during the move. One box of the dinner set didn't make it. It never arrived at our new house, so my mother had only three-quarters of the set: she had plates of different sizes and some serving pieces, but the tea cups and the soup bowls were missing. Often at family gatherings or when we would all sit down for a Thanksgiving or Christmas dinner, my mother would say something about the missing pieces and how she wished they had survived the trip. 83

When my mother died in 1983, I inherited Grandmother's dinner set. I, too, used the set on many special occasions, and I, too, wondered what had happened to the box, never expecting to see the missing pieces again. 84

I love to walk around antique shops and outdoor markets, hunting for treasures. It's great fun to walk up and down early in the morning, watching as the sellers spread their goods on the ground.

I hadn't been to an outdoor market in over a year, until one Sunday in 1993, for some reason I wanted to go. I crawled out of bed at 5 A.M. and drove an hour in the early morning darkness to the giant outdoor market in the suburbs. I walked up and down, and after a couple of hours I was thinking about leaving. I turned the last corner and took a few steps down the row, when I noticed some dishes scattered on the ground. I saw that they were hand-painted with forget-me-nots! I raced over to look at them more closely and carefully picked up a cup and a bowl... forget-me-nots! Exactly like Grandmother's dinner set, with the same delicate strokes and the same thin gold bands around the edges. I looked at the rest of the items — there were the cups! The bowls! They really were Grandmother's! 85

86 The dealer had noticed my excitement, and when she came over, I told her the story of the missing box. She said the cups and bowls had come from an estate sale in Lakewood — the next town over from where we had lived when I was a child. She had questioned the owners about the cups and bowls and they said that they had found them in a box in a closet. They had been there "forever."

87 I left the market that day, loaded with my amazing treasure. Even now, six years later, I am filled with wonder that so many things came together to let me find the missing pieces. What would have happened if I had woken later? What gave me the idea to go to the market on that particular day? What if I hadn't turned that last corner, choosing instead to leave and rest my sore feet?

Last week I had a party for some friends. I proudly served soup in those beautiful bowls that had been missing for so long.

Complete the note by filling in [1] to [5].

What happened to Grandmother's dinner set	
During the move to Colorado, [1]	
〈Plates and Serving Pieces〉	〈Tea Cups and Soup Bowls〉
· The author's mother used them. ⬇ · After the author lost her mother, [2]. ⬇ · They were used on many special occasions.	· They had been in a box in a closet [3]. ⬇ · They were sold at an estate sale. ⬇ · They were on sale at a giant outdoor market. ⬇ · The author recognized them as her grandmother's because [4]. ⬇ · [5].

問 1 [1]

① all pieces of the dinner set were delivered safely
② Grandmother painted a quarter of her dinner set
③ one of the four boxes of the hand-painted dinner set disappeared
④ the author's mother lost some precious plates

問 2 [2]

① she almost never used her grandmother's dinner set
② she received the remaining parts of the dinner set
③ she searched for the missing pieces, thinking that she would find them
④ she wondered why her mother had left the dinner set

問 3 [3]

① in the author's house in Elmira for a long time
② since the author moved from Colorado
③ until an outdoor market seller found them
④ until being discovered by the author

問 4 [4]

① she found the missing box with them
② the owners told her that they had found them in a closet
③ they were decorated in the same style
④ they were found near the house where she used to live

問 5 [5]

① The author felt relieved to find her friends had owned them
② The author felt they were too valuable to use
③ The author let her friends use them
④ The author went looking for them at the market again

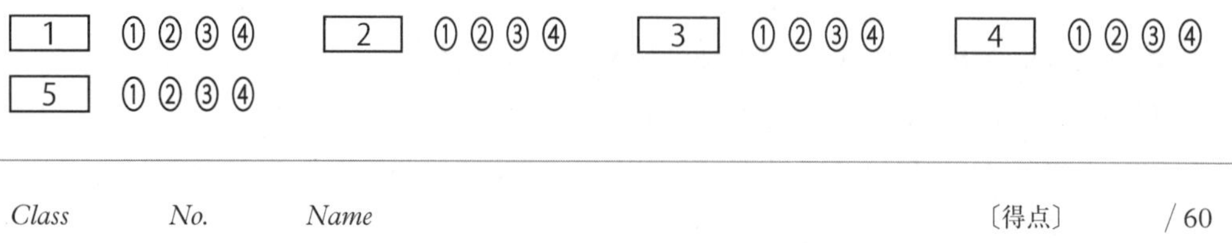

MEMO

Training 19

▶ 第6問A形式（長文読解・情報整理）

目標時間： 14分（挑戦12分）
総語数 ： 730 words
難易度 ： ★★★

You found the following article in a science magazine and made notes about it. (各15点) 88

While engineers in most of the world try to make robots that perform specific and usually unpleasant tasks, Japanese engineers are always trying to make machines more human. Japan has been the leader of the industrial robot market for the past two decades, and engineers are now working on a new generation of robots that will serve as friends, pets, and social workers. Their goal is to create an intelligent environment in which robots and humans can interact in everyday life. 89

There are still technical issues that hamper the manufacture of robots that are easy to live with — everything from understanding speech and gestures to making eye contact and having an awareness of human behavior. It will take more time to solve all of these issues, but the first such robots are already starting to appear. For example, guests at the World Expo in Shanghai, China were welcomed by robots that were able to show the guests their way. One company presented a dancing robot. Although these robots were a big improvement over robots of the past, they are still just the beginning of what is possible. 90

However, getting robots to understand real-life human speech may be the hardest job. More specifically, separating spoken words from background noises and understanding language at the same time has proved to be a big problem. For this reason, scientists are trying to give robots the ability — other than just understanding individual words — to understand the whole of what people are telling them. One new technology is intended to help robots understand the relationships among humans. For example, robots could be programmed to note how long people spend with each other in a room and to take into account friendships among people when communicating with them. Understanding the variety of gestures and signs that people use would help, too. 91

Robots could get information from the Internet, portable computers, or even television. They might gather additional data from microphones or sensors, noting where someone likes to eat, or what he or she is interested in. Wireless 92 identification (ID) tags are another potential source of information which would allow robots to identify people and acquire information about them. This idea was tested at an elementary school in which students who had been equipped with ID tags were surprised when the robots greeted them by name.

93 The emphasis on the future function of robots as companions and helpers seems to be deeply Japanese. The reason may have much to do with Japanese popular culture, where robots, like the cartoon cat Doraemon, tend to be portrayed as helpful and friendly. In fact, the tendency to regard lifelike machines as unthreatening may have deeper roots in Japan's Shinto culture, where objects ranging from teapots to samurai swords can have souls. The Japanese government is already promoting projects that have social applications, like nursing or childcare. This may well give a push to the development of more human-like robots because if robots are doing social work, they will have to look and act much more like people than they do now.

NOTES

Paragraph 1: The goal of engineers in Japan is to create robots that are [1].

Paragraph 3: One way robots might be able to overcome language barriers is to learn to [2].

Paragraph 5: [3].

→ The main idea of this passage is that [4].

問 1 Choose the best option for [1].

① able to interact with people in a more human way

② better at solving key problems in intelligent environments

③ skilled at overcoming scientific problems in the laboratory

④ willing to do jobs that people are unwilling to do

問 2 Choose the best option for [2].

① form true and lasting friendships with human beings

② program themselves to help people communicate with each other

③ recognize and understand human actions and interactions

④ respond more quickly to a human's touch

問 3 Choose the best option for [3].

① Japanese popular culture has produced many kinds of robots that are doing social work

② robots may one day take jobs away from the Japanese workforce

③ the Japanese government is promoting the idea that robots can and should have souls

④ the traditional Japanese view of objects has influenced the Japanese people's view of robots

問 4 Choose the best option for [4].

① it is necessary for robots to communicate with human beings

② Japan is unique in that its engineers try to develop human-like robots

③ robots could be a threat to people who are not familiar with Japanese popular culture

④ word-noise separation is the biggest challenge engineers in the world are facing now

[1] ① ② ③ ④　[2] ① ② ③ ④　[3] ① ② ③ ④　[4] ① ② ③ ④

Class　*No.*　*Name*　〔得点〕　/ 60

MEMO

Training 20

▶ 第 6 問 B 形式（長文読解・情報整理）

目標時間：　14 分（挑戦 12 分）
総語数　：　740 words
難易度　：　★★★

Your group is preparing a poster presentation entitled "The Use of Fire and Human History," using information from the magazine article below. 94

（各15点、問4は完答）

Of all the natural elements, fire seems to fascinate people like no other, and legends and myths about fire can be found in most cultures. For instance, a famous Greek myth from ancient times tells of how fire was stolen from the gods in heaven and brought to earth. Going even further back in time, pieces of fire-hardened cooking pots and burnt bones have been found in East Africa that date back at least one hundred thousand years. 95

The earliest humans did not know how to start a fire, so it is likely that they obtained it through natural events, such as fires caused by lightning, or from forest fires. Desperate to save this fire, our ancestors might have tried to preserve it by setting fire to pieces of wood and then trying to keep them burning continuously. However, this would not have been effective because early humans rarely stayed in one place for very long, and any fires they had been using would go out when they moved from one location to another. Then, probably by chance, one of our early ancestors discovered that sparks are produced when stones are hit against each other, and the making of fire was revolutionized. 96

The lives of early humans changed forever from the moment the first person discovered how to make fire. They found it could be used to provide warmth against cold, light in darkness, and protection against enemies great and small. It could also be used to prepare and preserve the meat from animals they had caught, to harden clay into pots, to shape metals into tools, to clear land for planting, and to hollow logs to make buildings. Indeed, it is difficult to imagine what life today would be like if humans had not mastered the use of fire. 97

History shows that although fire is incredibly useful, it can also be destructive, and there are stories from all parts of the ancient world of whole communities being destroyed by fire. Later, by the beginning of the Middle Ages, towns began to appear in Europe with large buildings constructed of wood. People at this time were worried about the danger of unattended fires, so many towns and villages adopted the practice of reminding their citizens to cover their fires at night. The English king, Alfred, was so worried about fire safety that he passed a law in 876 requiring all fires in the city of Oxford to be covered every day on the ringing 98 of a church bell at 7 p.m. In 1068, King William extended this law, called the curfew law, to the whole of England, but he also prohibited people from gathering outside their homes after dark. This law was very unpopular because it was clearly intended to control people's movements, rather than to prevent fires. The curfew law was repealed by King Henry I in 1100, but the ringing of "curfew bells," as they became known, continued in some churches for more than seven hundred years.

99 Who the first fire user was is a secret lost to history. But, whoever it was, the mastery of fire has shaped our lives more, perhaps, than any other discovery in human history.

The Use of Fire and Human History

■ Ancient humans and fire

・The earliest evidence of fire: [1]

・Humans used fires in nature

⇓ Revolution : humans [2]

・Humans found how to start a fire

→ Humans began using fire to [3] and so on

■ The rise of fire safety

TIME	EVENT
Beginning of the Middle Ages	[4]
876	[5]
1068	[6]
1100	[7]

■ The influence of fire

・Using fire has fundamentally shaped our lives

問 1 Which of the following is evidence of fire being used by humans? [1]

① a Greek myth

② a story from India

③ cave paintings in France

④ items found in Africa

問 2 Choose the best option to complete the poster. [2]

① found a way to keep a fire burning continuously
② had a constant supply of fire
③ happened to see a small flash of light when striking together two hard things
④ sparked the forest fire by hitting two stones

問 3 Choose the best option to complete the poster. [3]

① catch wild animals
② choose wood for making houses
③ make farmland
④ prevent farm animals from escaping

問 4 Put the events into the boxes [4] ～ [7] in order that they happened.

① Church bells began ringing in the evening
② Large wooden constructions were built
③ People could not come together outside their homes
④ The law was canceled

1	① ② ③ ④	2	① ② ③ ④	3	① ② ③ ④	4	① ② ③ ④
5	① ② ③ ④	6	① ② ③ ④	7	① ② ③ ④		

Class *No.* *Name* 〔得点〕 / 60

NAVI BOOK

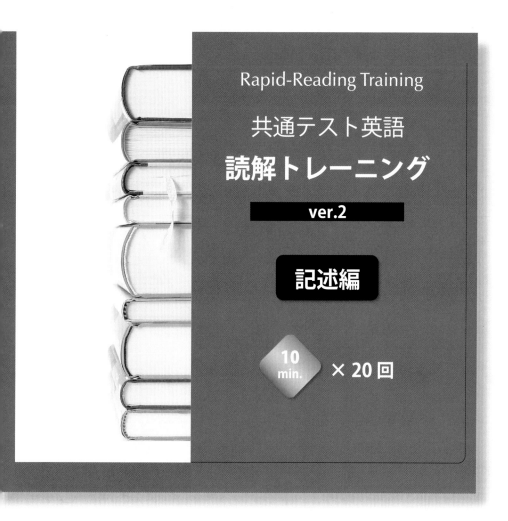

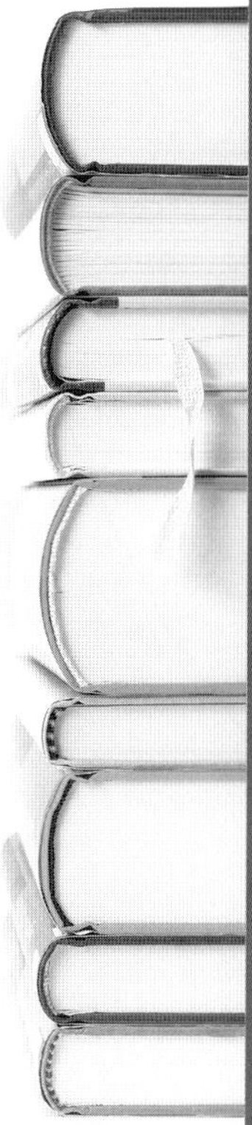

Rapid-Reading Training

共通テスト英語

読解トレーニング

ver.2

記述編

10 min. × 20 回

第 1 問 A
第 1 問 B

第 2 問 A
第 2 問 B

第 3 問 A
第 3 問 B

第 4 問

第 5 問

第 6 問 A
第 6 問 B

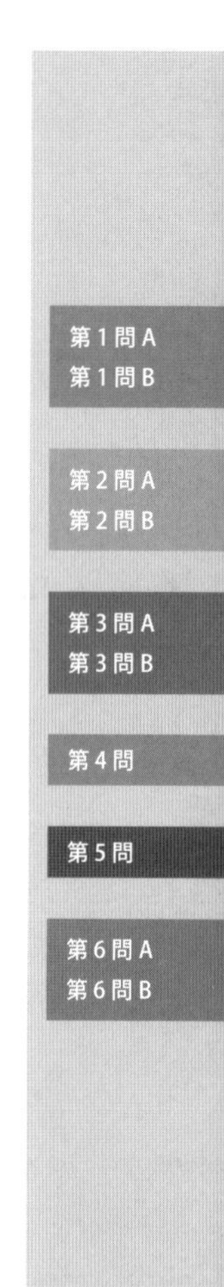

ÉMILE

NAVI BOOK

Rapid-Reading Training
共通テスト英語
読解トレーニング
ver.2
記述編
10 min.
× 20 回

≫ ナビブックの構成

「ナビブック」は共通テスト形式の問題を解いた後の学習効率を高める「再読」をするための冊子です。

各課は「精読問題」「重要語句」の２つのパートで構成されています。

精読問題

・先に解いた共通テスト形式の問題とは異なる別問題です。
・読解のポイントとなる箇所が主に記述問題で問われています。

重要語句

・全20課で覚えておきたい重要な語句の確認問題があります。
・解答書の語句の欄で確認することができます。

〈その他〉

◆ **各課の英文について**

本書で収録されている英文素材と同じものです。ただし、Training 8, 9, 10, 18, 19, 20の6課分は、英文素材のみを掲載しています。

◆ **本書設問解答欄（右頁上段）について**

本書の共通テスト形式の設問の解答を書き込む欄です。本ナビブックを提出物にする場合にはこちらをご利用ください。

》目次

*「総語数」 問題文と設問選択肢の合計（概数）

Training 1 《第 1 問 A 形式》

You received an email about a conference that you expect to attend next month. 1

From: John Martin <Jmartin@itconf.org> 2

To: All members

Date: July 25, 2019

Subject: Conference in Cardiff

Dear Colleagues, 3

I am writing to tell you about the next Computers in Education conference, which is being held in Cardiff on the 25th and 26th of August. At the conference, there will be **(A)**presentations on topics ranging from Internet-based learning to the latest educational software for children. And with more presentations than ever before, this year's event promises to be the best yet.

Further information can be found on our website (www.itconf.org). The site also has an online form that you can use to register for the conference. **(B)**Simply fill out the form, which is the same as the paper-based one used last year, and we will send you the final program by mail, together with a map of the conference area. 4

Some of you reported problems finding reasonable accommodations at last year's conference. I'm happy to say that the Cardiff Grand Hotel is offering us **(C)**special low rates this year. Although the hotel is some distance from the conference facility, it is right in the center of the city. The offer is, however, limited to those who make reservations directly with the hotel before August 10th. I look forward to seeing you next month in Cardiff. 5

John Martin

◇本書設問解答欄 1 ____ 2 ____ 3 ____

1. 下線部（A）の具体的な内容を日本語で２つ答えなさい。

- ____________________
- ____________________

2. 下線部（B）を和訳しなさい。

____

____

____

3. 下線部（C）の料金で利用するための条件を日本語で説明しなさい。

____

____

重要語句　（答えは解答解説書「語句」欄の赤字を参照）

range from A to B	…………	(h　　)	～を開催する
report	…………	(　　) to *do*	～する見込みがある
reasonable	…………	(f　　)(　　)	
offer A B	…………		～に記入する
facility	…………	(d　　)	距離
look forward to *doing*	…………	(m　　) a (r　　)	
previous	…………		予約する
include	…………	(a　　)	（～に）出席する
contact	…………	(　　) in (　　) with ～	
close to ～	…………		～と連絡を取る

Training 2 《第 1 問 B 形式》

You visited your school's website and found the following post. 6

The First Annual Speech Contest 7

Students here can now choose to take math, science, history, home economics and PE in English. Next year, we will start several English-only club activities, too. (A)By gathering students from both Japan and other countries who are interested in global education, we can become truly international. (**B**) the theme, 'Join our worlds together', we would like to introduce a speech contest. Current students and past graduates may enter. The event will be broadcast live on our website and the winner's speech will be used in our promotion video and in local TV commercials.

Theme	'Join our worlds together' – how to attract globally minded pupils
Place	School main hall (Map)
Date/Time	March 31st, 2019 11:00-15:30
Timing	Speech ... 10 minutes maximum Q&A ... 5 minutes
Presentation	Slides and images may be used but limited to 8 in total
Application	All entries must be in by March 8th, 2019. Please email a 150-word written or video summary of your speech for selection purposes. All ten final entries will be given a guided tour of global giant ATK Marketing.
Judges	School Principal, Professor Al Brown (International King University), ATK Marketing President Michael Taniguchi
Prizes	First Prize to Third Prize: 25000 yen gift card. The winner will be granted a 5-day summer internship at ATK Marketing.

◇本書設問解答欄 1 ____ 2 ____ 3 ____

1. 下線部（A）を和訳しなさい。

____

____

2. 空所（B）に入れるのに適切な語句を 1 つ選びなさい。

① Use

② Used

③ Using

④ We use

3. この投稿に応募する際に必要な条件を 3 つ日本語で答えなさい。

- ______________________________
- ______________________________
- ______________________________

4. コンテストで優勝したときに得られるものを日本語で答えなさい。

____

____

重要語句　　（答えは解答解説書「語句」欄の赤字を参照）

following	…………	(g　　)	～を集める
annual	…………	(t　　)	テーマ、主題
maximum	…………	(c　　)	現在の
application	…………	(a　　)	～を引きつける
grant A B	…………	(　　)	要約
hand A in[in A]	…………	(　　) **in A**	A を招き入れる、呼び込む
opportunity	…………		
		(r　　)	答える、応じる

Training 3 《第2問A形式》

You are a member of the arts and crafts club at school, and you want to make something popular overseas. On a website, you found a guide for making a craft design that looks interesting. 8

Craft Time 9

Hours of fun all year round. Educational but also (　　A　　) kids use their imagination and design skills, too.

Ocean in an Egg Box

You will need

A　Egg boxes (6 egg size)　　Blue paint　　Glitter glue　　Old newspaper

B　Sponge paper (can be bought at arts shops)　　colored card　　scissors

C　Small shells and stones (adult help needed for small children)
jewel stickers　　tape　　glue　　string

Instructions

Step 1: Make A

1. Lay the newspaper on a table to prevent stains and damage.
2. Paint the insides of the egg box. (10 minutes per box)
3. Cover with glitter glue. Dry for 20 minutes.

Step 2: Make B

1. Meanwhile, cut out seaweed shapes from the sponge paper.
2. Draw some fish on the colored card and cut them out.
(Photos of seaweed and fish are fine if you can't draw.) (approx. 5 minutes)

Step 3: Make C adding them to A with B

1. Glue the shells, stones, seaweed shapes and jewel stickers in the box. Warning: Pressing too hard will break the delicate shells.
2. (B)Hang the fish from the top of the box with string for a swimming effect. (approx. 10 minutes)

==

REVIEW & COMMENTS

Busypapa ***November 18, 2017 at 22:37***

(C)Best thing to do on a rainy day. Fun for all, even my teenage sons loved it! Good as a safe place for my car keys and change.

kinder@garten ***June 4, 2019 14:21***

A big hit with my 1st graders, helped me teach them fish and sea animals. (D)I used blue tissue paper to line the box, it saved time on painting.

◇本書設問解答欄 1 ____ 2 ____ 3 ____ 4 ____ 5 ____

1. 空所 (A) に入れるのに適切な語を 1 つ選びなさい。

① enables

② gets

③ lets

④ tells

2. 下線部 (B) を和訳しなさい。

3. 下線部 (C) を和訳しなさい。

4. 下線部 (D) の意味として最も適切なものを 1 つ選びなさい。

① This person drew blue lines on the box.

② This person did not use glitter glue.

③ This person painted the tissue paper blue.

④ This person made the craft faster.

重 要 語 句 (答えは解答解説書「語句」欄の赤字を参照)

educational		(i)	想像力
let O *do*		( )	技能、技術
lay		( )	～を妨げる
delicate		( )	損傷
hang		(m)	その間
effect		(s) time ( ) ～	
creative			～の時間を節約する
		( ) to ～	～によると

Training 4 《第2問B形式》

Your assistant language teacher (ALT) gave you an article to help you prepare for the debate at the end of term. A part of this article with one of the comments is shown below. 10

Uniform Freedom for all ages 11

By *Julian Shortland*, Virginia Beach
18 JULY 2018 ・11:18 AM

Elementary schools in Petersburg are making school uniforms optional for all grades. (A) This means younger students will now follow the same system already in place in middle and high schools. Since some parents have recently bought new uniforms, children are still free to wear them if they wish. Students will have to follow educational board rules which include no sunglasses or headwear, pajamas, oversized clothes and fashion with bad language or shocking designs.

The change started because of (B) school staff complaints. Teacher Maria Gonzalez said, "We wasted hours scolding them about their uniforms. Besides, they can learn just as well in their own clothes." She added, "We sent out a questionnaire to parents and 85% of them agreed that uniforms were not necessary." 12

(C) this, some mothers and fathers have stated, "Not all kids can keep up. Poorer ones may be bullied for being unfashionable. Uniforms help pupils become part of a team." In addition, a local politician said, "There are security concerns, too. Last winter when a Petersburg student got lost, police soon found him on security cameras as he was wearing a fixed set of clothing and colors." 13

34 Comments 14

Latest

Marcia Tilsbury 20 July 2018 ・22:46PM

(D) Kids do need to be able to express their characters and clothing is a great way to show their own style. There are plenty of other chances to do this on vacation, weekends and public holidays, though.

◇本書設問解答欄 1 ____ 2 ____ 3 ____ 4 ____ 5 ____

1. 下線部（A）を、This の内容を明らかにしながら和訳しなさい。

2. 下線部（B）について、本文で述べられている内容を 2 点、日本語で答えなさい。

-
-

3. 空所（C）に入れるのに適切な語句を 1 つ選びなさい。

① As a result of ② Because of ③ Despite ④ In addition to

4. 下線部（D）を和訳しなさい。

重要語句 （答えは解答解説書「語句」欄の赤字を参照）

freedom		(f)	～に従う
optional		(s)	制度
complaint		(c)	変化
waste A *doing*		(b) of ～	～の理由で
despite		in (a)	さらに
state		(s)	安全
keep up		(c)	懸念、不安
get lost		(e)	～を表現する
character		(w)	方法
chance		(p) of ～	十分な～
belong to ～		make (a) (s)	選択する
thanks to ～		in (f) of ～	～に賛成で

Training 5 《第3問A形式》

You are in an English class listening to Mei talk about her experience participating in the welcome party for international center students. 15

My name is Mei Chen. I'm from Beijing, China. I'd like to talk about the welcome party for the international center students. The party was called for 6 p.m., so I made sure that I was there a few minutes before 6:00. I wore a dress, but most of the students wore casual clothing. Some of them even came in jeans and T-shirts. There were some puzzle games first. After that they served dinner. They had all types of grilled meat and vegetables for dinner. The food didn't have any spices or sauces, so I thought it was all a little too plain. (A)<u>They had some sort of a fruit drink the teachers called "punch" that was pretty good, though.</u> Next, the teachers in charge made a few speeches and then we had some entertainment. Some of the students from Eastern Europe did some folk dancing, which was really nice. A friend from my English class, Antonio, sang and played the drums. After Antonio performed, one of the teachers passed out song sheets. (B)<u>The teacher played the guitar and we all sang the songs.</u> That was a lot of fun. Some of the students went out after the party, but I said I was tired and went back to my room. 16

You are in an English class listening to Antonio talk about his experience participating in the welcome party for international center students. 17

I'm Antonio Wakabayashi from Sao Paulo, Brazil. The other night, they had a party to welcome all the new students. (C)<u>I thought it was a little early to start a dinner party at 6:00, so I figured it was okay to be a little late.</u> The food was very nice. They had asked me to sing a few Brazilian songs, so I performed. I sang and played the drums. Most of the other presentations were very interesting. After the student performances, we had a sing-along with Mr. Templeton. He played old favorites on the guitar. That was fun, but I felt disappointed because I suggested some songs and he didn't play them. In the beginning there were only a few people singing, but by the time we finished almost everyone had joined in with us. The party ended at 8:30. Since it was still so early, some of us decided to go out. I invited my friend Mei to go with us, but she said she was too tired. I think she's actually shy and scared to go out with a group. (D)<u>We enjoyed singing so much that we decided to go to a karaoke place so we could keep singing.</u> After that, everyone wanted to go to a pizza shop. I was still kind of full from dinner, but I managed to eat two pieces of pizza. 18

◇本書設問解答欄 1 ____ 2 ____ 3 ____ 4 ____

1. 下線部（A）を和訳しなさい。

____

____

2. 下線部（B）の状態を表すのに最も近い語を１語、アントニオの発言から抜き出しなさい。

____

3. 下線部（C）から推測できる英文を１つ選びなさい。

① Antonio thought that the party would not finish on time.

② Antonio thought that being on time for the party was very important.

③ Antonio was a little late for the party.

④ Antonio was surprised to find that Mei had already arrived.

4. 下線部（D）を和訳しなさい。

____

____

重要語句 （答えは解答解説書「語句」欄の赤字を参照）

make (　　　) that ～ 確実に～するようにする	**(s　　　　　　)** （食事）を出す
some sort of ～ …………	**(e　　　　　　)** 余興、娯楽
in charge …………	**(p　　　　　　)** 演奏する
pass out ～ …………	**(f　　　　　) that ～** ～だと考える
presentation …………	**(f　　　　　　)** お気に入り
performance …………	**(s　　　　　　)** ～を提案する
disappointed …………	**(j　　　　　) in with ～** ～に加わる
actually …………	***be* (s　　　　) to *do*** ～するのが怖い
shy …………	**(m　　　　) to *do*** なんとか～する
	(c　　　　　　) about ～ ～について不満を述べる

Training 6 《第 3 問 B 形式》

The following story is about Hideo and his family. 19

Hideo is a student at a college, studying animals. He hopes to work in a hospital in the future, practicing animal-assisted therapy. He became interested in animal-related jobs because he had often watched his grandfather, Tomozo, happily taking good care of his dog. 20

Tomozo was once hospitalized with a heart attack at the age of 70. After he came home from the hospital, he barely went outside and stopped working in the fields. He spent all day just watching television. His family became increasingly worried about this change. **(A)**One day Hideo's mother suggested to Tomozo that he keep a dog for company. 21

When the dog came, Tomozo looked very happy. He named the dog Hana. He seemed to enjoy taking care of her every day. There was a gradual change in his complexion. The doctor had said that Tomozo might have another heart attack at any moment, but he seemed to get healthier after Hana arrived. Tomozo spent more time outdoors and he even sometimes did some light work in the fields. She was with him when he read newspapers and listened to the radio. 22

Ten years later, Hana died. Soon after her death, Tomozo passed away at the age of 80. **(B)**The doctor said that he might not have lived that long without Hana. Hideo also felt that Hana had had a good effect on Tomozo. 23

◇本書設問解答欄 1 ____ 2 ____ 3 ____

1. ヒデオが動物に関する仕事に興味を持つようになった原因を、本文に従って簡潔に述べなさい。

____

2. 下線部（A）を、that が導く名詞節に注意しながら日本語にしなさい。

____

3. 下線部（B）を和訳しなさい。

____

重要語句　（答えは解答解説書「語句」欄の赤字を参照）

take care of ～	…………	become (i　　) (i　　) ～	～に興味を持つ
heart attack	…………		
at the age of ～	…………	(b　　)	ほとんど～ない
become worried about ～	…………	(f　　)	畑
for company	…………	(s　　) O *doing*	O を～して過ごす
at any moment	…………		
sometimes	…………	(i　　)	だんだん
soon after ～	…………	(s　　)	～を提案する
pass away	…………	(n　　)	～を名づける
have an effect on ～	…………	(g　　)	徐々の
(p　　)	～を実施する	(l　　)	軽い

再読編

Training 7《第４問形式》

You are in a class, listening to Emma and Jasper give presentations on their joint research. 24

Emma: Over the past few decades, travel in Great Britain has become much easier, with faster and more fuel-efficient cars and more convenient public transportation systems. What is more, many households now own two cars. Given (A)<u>this background</u>, one might expect that more people are traveling farther and more frequently. However, according to a survey conducted by the Department for Transport in 2010, people in Britain are traveling less often than before. This trend is true for all modes of transportation, including walking. 25

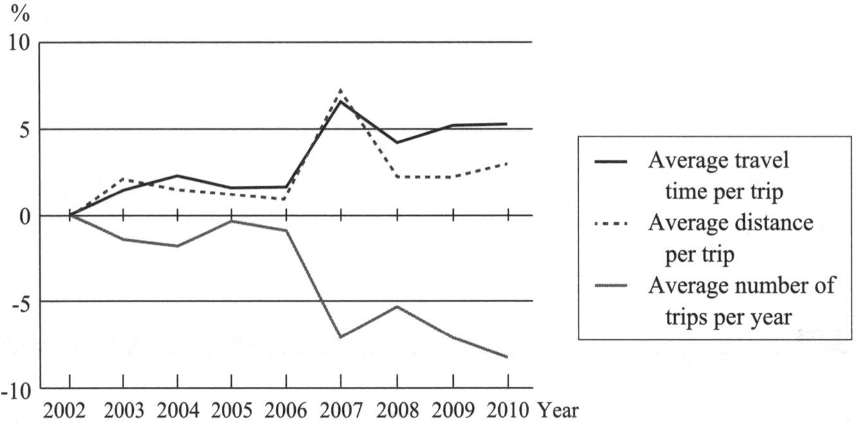

Figure 1. Travel patterns in Britain 2002 - 2010 (percent change).

The number of trips made per person each year did begin to increase in the 1970s but then started to level off in the 1990s. (B)<u>Focusing on the period from 2002 to 2010 (Figure 1), one observes that, while both the averages in travel time and trip distance increased, the average number of trips per person dropped.</u> The average travel time increased by just over 5% from 21.8 minutes in 2002 to 22.9 minutes in 2010, and the average trip distance increased by almost 3% from 6.8 miles to 7.0 miles. On the other hand, the average number of trips fell by approximately 8%. People traveled an average of 1,047 times in 2002, but they made only 960 trips in 2010. 26

Jasper: What happened in Great Britain to cause this? The decline in the number of trips between 2002 and 2010 can be partly accounted for by falls in shopping and visiting friends at their homes. On average, people made only 193 shopping trips per year in 2010, as opposed to 214 in 2002. Trips to visit friends at private homes declined from 123 to 103 per person per year during this period, whereas 27

◇本書設問解答欄 1 ____ 2 ____ 3 ____

the number of trips to meet friends at places other than their homes remained almost constant, at 48 in 2002 and 46 in 2010. The fewer trips for shopping and visiting friends at home may, in turn, be explained by certain changes in society that took place over the period surveyed.

1. 下線部（A）の内容を2点、簡潔な日本語で説明しなさい。

- ____________________
- ____________________

2. 下線部（B）を和訳しなさい。

____

____

3. ジャスパーがこの次に語る内容として、最も適切なものを1つ選びなさい。

① He compares the numbers of shopping trips and visits to friends' homes made in 2002 and 2010 by people in Britain.

② He explains how the society in Britain now demands that people travel more for business.

③ He explores social trends in Britain impacting the number of shopping trips and visits to friends' homes.

④ He lists reasons why one can expect people in Britain to travel more often using public transportation.

重 要 語 句　（答えは解答解説書「語句」欄の赤字を参照）

what is more	…………	(f　　)	頻繁に
household	…………	(c　　)	～を実施する
survey（名）	…………	(i　　)	～を含める
level off	…………	(o　　)	…………
focus on ～	…………		～（ということ）に気づく
approximately	…………	(a　　) for ～	…………
decline	…………		～（の理由）を説明する
as opposed to ～	…………	(w　　)	その一方で
other than ～	…………	(r　　)	依然として～のままである
take place	…………	(c　　)	一定の
(d　　)	10年	(c　　) to ～	～と比べると

Training 8 《第 5 問形式》

You read a story and made notes about it. 28

One of the most remarkable stories I know is about a man called Robertson McQuilkin. As a young man, he dreamed of becoming the president of Columbia Bible College in Columbia, South Carolina. He looked up to his father, who had held this position, and he hoped to take his father's place someday. 29

Robertson McQuilkin's dream came true. One day he did become the president of Columbia Bible College. When he became the president, he was convinced that he was called by God and was worthy of that position. 30

He worked as president of that college for a number of years, and he did very well and was respected and loved by many people. 31

Then one day Dr. McQuilken realized he had a tragedy on his hands. His wife began to show the symptoms of Alzheimer's disease. She became worse in a short time, and in a few months she was in terrible condition. **(A)**She not only lost her memory of much of their life together, but she was unable to even recognize him. She lost all awareness that he was her husband. 32

Robertson McQuilkin made his decision. He resigned the presidency of the college so he could give full-time care to his wife. Without question, he chose (**B1**) his job, (**B2**) his love for her. 33

There were some realists who told him there was no meaning in what he was doing. Anybody could take care of his poor wife, they told him, but not anybody could be president of the college. And after all, she didn't even recognize him when he came in the room to help her. 34

Then there were some religious people who said he was walking away from what God called him to do. He should carry out his social responsibility, which was more important, they said. 35

The man's answers were amazing. To the realists he admitted that his wife didn't know who he was. But **(C1)**that wasn't important, he told them. "**(D)**The really important thing was that I still knew who she was, and that I saw in her the same lovely woman I had married decades ago," he said. 36

Then he turned to the religious people. His words to them were even more profound: "There is only one thing more important than your job" he told them. "And **(C2)**that is a promise. And I promised to be there for her 'until death do us part.'" 37

◇本書解答欄 [1] ____ [2] ____ [3] ____ [4] ____

1. 下線部（A）を和訳しなさい。

____

____

2. 文脈から判断して、空所（B1）（B2）それぞれに入る適切な1語を書きなさい。

(B1) ______________

(B2) ______________

3. 下線部（C1）（C2）それぞれの指す内容を、簡潔な日本語で書きなさい。

(C1) ______________________________

(C2) ______________________________

4. 下線部（D）を和訳しなさい。

____

____

____

重要語句　　　（答えは解答解説書「語句」欄の赤字を参照）

remarkable		(t　　) *one's* (p　　)	～の後任になる
look up to ～			
tragedy		(c　　) (　　)	実現する
symptom		*be* (c　　) that ～	～を確信している
terrible			
awareness		*be* (w　　) of ～	～にふさわしい、～に値する
resign			
religious		(r　　)	～を尊敬する
social		(r　　)	～を認識する
responsibility		(c　　) out ～	～を遂行する
decade		(a　　)	～を認める
eventually		(p　　)	深みのある
(p　　)	学長	(a　　)	～を賞賛する
(p　　)	地位		

Training 9 《第 6 問 A 形式》

You are learning about sports science at school and preparing to give a presentation in class. You have found the article below and made notes about it. 38

In 1996, 200 million Americans watched the Summer Olympics in Atlanta on television. (A)Televised sports are so popular that they have created highly successful, all-sports television networks. In addition, they have led to an adult fitness boom, which has flourished as more and more people are exercising to keep themselves healthy and youthful. And today's American heroes are not politicians, business executives, or scientists. 39

How did sports become such an important aspect of American life? Let's start with the definition of "athlete." Baseball players and marathon runners are athletes, but chess and bridge players are not. This is because sports in modern society are competitive, rule-based activities that require physical skills. Athletes compete against themselves, another individual, an established record, or other teams. They may be amateurs who play purely for enjoyment, or (B)they may be professional athletes who are paid for their efforts and display their skills before a paying audience. 40

American sports history examines the development over time of athletic activities, particularly the emergence of specific sports which have their own rules and institutions. Why, for example, are there eleven players on a football team? The study of sports also analyzes the relationships between sports and social institutions, political and economic structures, geography, and group and individual behavior. For instance, why is baseball considered the national sport? How did American society shape the development of sports? How did the loss of public space influence the rise of sports? Finally, the study of sports also involves considering how sports have influenced American values and social behavior. 41

Until recently, historians rarely studied sports because it seemed trivial, or because they considered other topics to be more important. Furthermore, historians who wanted to study sports were often afraid that they could never get a job if they wrote research papers on sports. Even noted historians who wanted to study sports were worried that writing about it would mark them as researchers of an unimportant subject. 42

(C)Academic interest in sports history emerged in the early 1970s, encouraged by historians who began to realize that the study of sports explained certain central themes of American history, particularly class, race, and gender issues. Many realized that analyzing the myths, realities, symbols, and customs in sports provided an excellent means for examining and understanding American values and beliefs. 43

◇本書解答欄 1 ＿＿ 2 ＿＿ 3 ＿＿ 4 ＿＿

Today, sports history has expanded into a popular area of study, and it is no longer simply social history, but may also be economic history, urban history, political history, educational history, or cultural history, depending on the topics and questions under consideration.

1. 下線部（A）が生み出したものを 2 つ、本文中の英語を抜き出して答えなさい。

- ＿＿＿＿＿＿＿＿＿＿
- ＿＿＿＿＿＿＿＿＿＿

2. 下線部（B）を和訳しなさい。

＿＿＿＿＿＿＿＿＿＿

＿＿＿＿＿＿＿＿＿＿

3. 第 3 段落には the study of sports の内容として 3 項目が挙げられているが、②③に当たる内容を簡潔な日本語で答えなさい。

① スポーツ活動の発展、特に独自のルールと組織を持つ特定のスポーツの出現

② ＿＿＿＿＿＿＿＿＿＿

③ ＿＿＿＿＿＿＿＿＿＿

4. 下線部（C）を和訳しなさい。

＿＿＿＿＿＿＿＿＿＿

＿＿＿＿＿＿＿＿＿＿

＿＿＿＿＿＿＿＿＿＿

重 要 語 句　（答えは解答解説書「語句」欄の赤字を参照）

executive	…………	(a　　　　)	側面
definition	…………	(e　　　　)	～を確立する
competitive	…………	(e　　　　)	～を調査する
analyze	…………	(i　　　　)	制度
political	…………	(e　　　　)	出現する
structure	…………	(r　　　　)	人種
values	…………	under (　　　　)	検討中の
scholar	…………		
profitable	…………		

Training 10 《第 6 問 B 形式》

You are preparing a presentation on renewable energy. You are going to read the following magazine article to understand the state of wind power. 44

Wind is an increasingly valuable source of energy — helping to bring electricity into our lives. At the National Wind Technology Center (NWTC) in Colorado, scientists are working to improve wind-power technology and lower the cost of generating electricity. Generating power from the wind leaves no harmful waste products behind, says NWTC's Jim Johnson. Best of all, the supply is unlimited. "The wind is always blowing somewhere," says Johnson. 45

The potential for wind power is huge. But right now, the United States gets less than one tenth of a percent of its electricity from wind energy, Johnson says. Some experts say it's possible to increase that number to 20 percent or more. (A)In theory, North Dakota alone could supply one third of the country's energy if there were an efficient way to transport the energy to where it's needed. The U.S. Department of Energy estimates that the world's winds could generate 15 times the amount of energy now used around the globe, if only we could make good use of them. 46

Even so, there are some people who argue that wind energy production is far from perfect. (B)One of the biggest problems with wind is its unreliability. Though the wind might always be blowing somewhere at any time, there's no guarantee that it will blow all the time at any particular place. 47

(C)The faster and more often the wind blows, the cheaper and easier it is to get power from it. So wind farms tend to be built in the windiest places, such as Minnesota and Kansas. Unfortunately, these places are far from cities on the coast, where a large number of people live. There's still no good way to transport wind energy over long distances. 48

In addition, wind power plants are also thought to affect human health because the turbines create low-frequency sounds and other noise problems. There are also issues with durability, as there have been reports of large wind turbines falling down. These problems lead many to believe that wind power plants cannot be built in urban areas. 49

There's still a lot of research to be done on making sure that wind power does its job efficiently, safely and cheaply. However, wind power has the potential to make the world less dependent on coal and oil, and to help clean up the environment. 50

◇本書設問解答欄 1 ____ 2 ____ 3 ____ 4 ____ 5 ____ 6 ____

1. 下線部（A）を和訳しなさい。

2. 下線部（B）のように言える理由を、簡潔な日本語で答えなさい。

3. 下線部（C）を和訳しなさい。

4. 第6段落で述べられている、風力が持っている可能性を2つ、簡潔な日本語で答えなさい。

-
-

重要語句　　（答えは解答解説書「語句」欄の赤字を参照）

source		(v)	価値のある
electricity		(s)	供給、～を供給する
generate		in (t)	理論上は
harmful		(g)	地球、世界
potential		(a)	～と主張する、～を議論する
huge			
efficient		(g)	保証、～を保証する
at any time		*be* (d) (　　) ～	～に依存している
urban			
currently		(c)	特徴
		(l)	続く、持続する

Training 11 《第 1 問 A 形式》

The following texts are emails exchanged between John and Maria. 51

Hi Maria! 52

When we go shopping the day after tomorrow, why don't we meet in front of the department store at 4:00 P.M.? The websites say that the department store and the shopping mall are both open on the day, but should we check out the department store first? They have a wider selection of things we could buy for Mom, and their restaurants are better. They have a really good Italian restaurant, so the three of us should eat dinner there. The bus I'm taking is scheduled to arrive just before 4:00. I don't think there will be much traffic, so I'm pretty sure I'll be there on time, but there's a chance I may be a little late. Talk to Kate about it, and if there are any problems get in touch with me. Looking forward to seeing you!

John

Hi John! 53

Kate and I are both OK with that time, and Kate said that she will take the train that arrives about ten minutes before 4:00. I think we should go to the department store, too. She and I were talking about buying Mom a sweater she saw in the department store. Mom really likes that shop — but it's a little expensive, so let's go there first and check it out. The Italian restaurant also sounds great! **(A)**<u>I haven't had Italian food in a long time.</u> I'll go a little bit early and buy Mom a birthday card at the stationery shop in the shopping mall.

See you the day after tomorrow!

Maria

◇本書設問解答欄 1 ____ 2 ____

1. 本文の内容に合うように、空所に本文中の英語を１語ずつ入れなさい。

(1) John gets the information about the department store and the shopping mall on the ( ).

(2) John will go to the department store by ( ), and he suggests the possibility of his being a little ( ).

(3) What Maria will buy first is a ( ) ( ) for Mom.

2. 下線部（A）を和訳しなさい。

____

重 要 語 句 （答えは解答解説書「語句」欄の赤字を参照）

the day after tomorrow		***be*** **(s) to ～**	～する予定である
	....	**(a)**	到着する
in front of ～	....	**(pr)**	とても、かなり
check out	....	***be*** **(s)**	確信している
on time	....	**(c)**	可能性
get in touch with ～	....	**(p)**	問題
look forward to ～	....	**(e)**	高価な
a little bit	....	**(so)**	～に思える
stationery shop	....	**(pr)**	おそらく
be **certain about ～**	....	**(f)**	お気に入りの
distance	....		

Training 12 《第1問B形式》

You are planning to travel to New York. You found a website for a hotel. 54

Riverside Hotel 55

234 W 61st St. New York, NY 10032 Book online or call **0044-33-229938**

(A)The Riverside Hotel is located on the Upper West Side of New York, NY, and welcomes tourists and business people visiting the city. The hotel is one block away from the Museum of Natural History. Times Square is ten blocks from the hotel. Lincoln Center and Central Park are five blocks away. The front desk is available 24 hours a day and offers tour assistance.

Nightly Room Rates

Standard single room including breakfast : $98.00
Standard twin room including breakfast : $148.00
Check-in time — 3 pm Check-out time — 12 pm
Photo identification required upon check-in
No pets allowed

Driving Directions

From JFK International Airport : (Approximate distance to the hotel is 20 miles.)

- Take the Belt Parkway west to the Brooklyn Battery Tunnel.
- Take the West Side Highway north. Exit at 72nd St.
- At the second traffic light, turn right on 71st St. and go down to 61st St.
- The hotel is located on the left.

Parking

Why worry about your vehicle or struggle to find a convenient parking space in New York? (B)Take advantage of our convenient parking, which is located across the street from Grand Central Terminal, giving you easy access to trains, subway lines and the entire city. (C)Don't worry about your vehicle or rental car — our hotel parking is safe and secure, so you'll never waste time trying to locate your parking spot.

Parking cost : $20 per day.
If the vehicle requires two spaces, the guest will be charged for two cars.

Area Activities

Broadway ..... 2 blocks	**Central Park** ..... 5 blocks	**Times Square** ..... 10 blocks
Lincoln Center ..... 5 blocks	**Bronx Zoo** ..... 8.0 miles	**Statue of Liberty** ..... 1.5 miles

◇本書設問解答欄 [1] ____ [2] ____ [3] ____

1. 下線部（A）を和訳しなさい。

2. 下線部（B）を和訳しなさい。

3. 下線部（C）を和訳しなさい。

重要語句 （答えは解答解説書「語句」欄の赤字を参照）

welcome	(b)	〜を予約する
identification	(a)	利用できる
approximate	(d)	案内
struggle to *do*	(e)	出る、退出する
take advantage of 〜	(v)	乗り物
suburban	(e)	全体の
document	(l)	場所
round trip	(p)	〜を（見えるように）提示する
reservation	(i)	（身元）を確認する
	(d)	説明、描写

Training 13 《第2問A形式》

You are thinking of making a snack this weekend. On a website, you found a recipe that looks good. 56

My Favorite Recipes.com 57

Search My Favorite Recipes.com [ ] Search

Recipes | Cooking Tips | Measurements | Comments | Shop

Banana muffins

POSTED BY: Kim

SERVINGS: 12 muffins

INGREDIENTS:

3 bananas, mashed
1/4 teaspoon salt
1/2 cup butter, softened
1/4 cup milk
1/2 cup brown sugar
2 cups all-purpose flour
1 teaspoon baking powder
1 teaspoon baking soda
1/2 cup chopped walnuts
1 teaspoon vanilla
2 large eggs

DIRECTIONS:

1. Preheat oven to 375 degrees F (190 degrees C).
2. In your mixing bowl, mix together butter and brown sugar until the mixture is creamy. Add bananas, milk, eggs and vanilla, mixing well. Gently stir in flour, baking powder, soda and salt, until moistened. Add the walnuts. Pour the mixture into a muffin pan.
3. Bake at 375 degrees F for around 20 minutes, until a toothpick inserted into a muffin is dry when it comes out. Allow to cool in the pan for 5 minutes. Then place the muffins on a wire rack to finish cooling.

COMMENT ON / RATE THIS RECIPE 58

COMMENTS:

★★★★☆

I wanted lower calorie banana muffins so I combined this recipe with my favorite low-fat muffin recipe. I used 1/4 cup of unsweetened applesauce instead of the butter, used only 1 egg, and only half the sugar (1/4 cup). (A)The applesauce not only lowers the calories, it also makes the muffins taste even better.

Janet in Oklahoma

MORE COMMENTS...

◇本書設問解答欄 1 ____ 2 ____ 3 ____ 4 ____ 5 ____

1. キムのレシピに従うとき、手順が正しい順番に並んでいるものを選びなさい。

① mash bananas → add the walnuts → insert a toothpick → use milk and eggs

② mash bananas → use milk and eggs → add the walnuts → insert a toothpick

③ use milk and eggs → insert a toothpick → mash bananas → add the walnuts

④ use milk and eggs → mash bananas → add the walnuts → insert a toothpick

2. ジャネットは今回、どのような方針で彼女のマフィンを作ったのか、日本語で説明しなさい。

____

____

3. 下線部（A）を和訳しなさい。

____

____

重要語句 （答えは解答解説書「語句」欄の赤字を参照）

recipe	....	(t　　　)	ヒント、秘けつ
measurement	....	(p　　　)	～を投稿する
ingredient	....	(s　　　)	（1 回分の）分量
mash	....	(c　　　)	～を切り刻む
moisten	....	(s　　　)	～を柔らかくする
pour A into B	....	(d　　　)	指示、やり方
bake	....	(m　　　)	混ぜ合わせたもの
insert	....	(g　　　)	やさしく、静かに
combine A with B	....	(s　　　) in ～	～を入れてかき混ぜる
instead of ～	....	(p　　　)	～を置く

再読編

Training 14 《第2問B形式》

Your teacher showed you a school website to help you prepare for the debate in the next class. A part of this website with one of the comments is shown below. 59

Changes in School Rules 60

The school officials are considering allowing students to ride motorbikes or scooters to school. Some parents approve of this plan, while others are opposed. Ms. Singh, whose son is in the eleventh grade, made the following statement:

"I would be very concerned for my son's safety if students were allowed to ride motorbikes to school. First, there isn't enough space at school to park them. Second, motorbikes are expensive to buy and maintain. And most of all, they're dangerous. High school students are not ready to ride such risky machines. (A)Have you ever seen how carelessly they act when they ride their bicycles? They use their cell phones, eat and drink, and even read books, all while flying through the streets. They're much too irresponsible. With a motorbike, they could really cause damage for themselves or someone else." 61

Mr. Hutchins, the father of a twelfth-grader, said the following: 62

"I understand the worries that many parents have about safety. However, for families like ours that live far away from school, life would be much more convenient if students could ride motorbikes. My wife and I both have full-time jobs, so we're much too busy to drive our daughter to school. We practiced many hours with her, so we have no doubt that she is very careful when she rides. My proposal is that students be given a basic test concerning the rules of the road. Only if they pass, they can ride their motorbikes. (B)If not, they have to start over from scratch."

34 Comments 63

Latest

Ms. Yang, the mother of an 11th-grade student 20 July 2018 · 22:46PM

I'm not sure how we can solve the problem of parking space, but I think students should be (**C**) to ride motorbikes to school with certain conditions. My daughter is on the basketball team, and she gets home from school late every day. There usually aren't any other people walking in our neighborhood, and I worry that it's too dangerous for her to walk home on the dark street from the bus stop. Why don't we let students ride motorbikes to school only if they have permission from their parent or guardian, and their homeroom teacher or the teacher responsible for their extracurricular activity?

◇本書設問解答欄 1 ____ 2 ____ 3 ____ 4 ____ 5 ____

1. 下線部 (A) を、they が指すものを明らかにして和訳しなさい。

____

____

2. Ms. Singh がバイク通学に反対する根拠を、簡潔な日本語で 3 つ答えなさい。

- ______________________________
- ______________________________
- ______________________________

3. 下線部 (B) の具体的な内容を日本語で説明しなさい。

____

4. 空所 (C) に入れるのに適切な語を 1 つ選びなさい。

① allowed ② forbidden ③ opposed ④ restricted

重 要 語 句 (答えは解答解説書「語句」欄の赤字を参照)

official (名詞) ....
most of all ....
risky ....
irresponsible ....
proposal ....
concerning ~ ....
from scratch ....
neighborhood ....
permission ....
responsible ....
ban (動詞) ....

(a) O to *do* O に~することを許す
(a) of ~ ~に賛成する
be (o) ~に反対である
(s) 主張
be (c) for ~ ~を心配する
(d) 疑い
(c) ある、一定の
(c) 条件
(l) O *do* O に~させる
(i) ~を巻き込む、~に関わる

Training 15 《第 3 問 A 形式》

You are interested in international volunteer activities. You are going to read the following article to understand what JOCV is. 64

JOCV（Japan Overseas Cooperation Volunteers）is a program that sends young people (age 20-39) overseas as volunteers. It started in 1966. Since then, more than 45,000 people have been sent to **(A)**about 90 countries, where people suffer from poverty, hunger, diseases, poor education and many other problems. The number of volunteers increased from about 111 in 1966 to about 1,800 in 2019. 65

What kinds of work are the volunteers engaged in? The volunteers were divided into seven work fields in 1966. Almost half of the volunteers worked in only one of the seven fields, *Agriculture, Forestry and Fisheries. In the second place was Civil Engineering, and in the third was Maintenance. However, the situation has changed in the last 50 years. In 2019, the largest number of volunteers worked in the field of Education and Culture. The second place was taken by *Health and Hygiene, followed by Social Welfare 66

There are various activities in each field, and they have been expanding in a variety of ways. For example, **(B)**activities related to HIV/AIDS awareness, which did not exist 50 years ago, are now a *crucial part of Health and Hygiene. As for Education and Culture, science and math teachers are badly needed. In some countries you can be a science or math teacher without a teacher's qualification. The participants are not limited only to experts such as nurses or car mechanics. At JOCV young people get opportunities to make good use of their hobbies or interests to help promote world peace and friendship. 67

* Agriculture, Forestry and Fisheries「農林・水産」 Health and Hygiene「保健衛生」 crucial「重要な」

◇本書設問解答欄 1 ____ 2 ____ 3 ____

1. 下線部（A）の国々では、どのような問題があると書かれているか。日本語で説明しなさい。

____

2. 1966年と2019年において、最も多くのボランティアが従事したJOCVの活動分野はそれぞれ何か。本文から抜き出しなさい。

（1966年）______________________________

（2019年）______________________________

3. 下線部（B）を和訳しなさい。

____

____

重要語句 （答えは解答解説書「語句」欄の赤字を参照）

suffer from ～	....	(o　　　)	海外の［へ］
hunger	....	(c　　　)	協力
disease	....	(p　　　)	貧困
education	....	(d　　　) O (i　　　) ～	
be engaged in ～	....		O を～に分ける
agriculture	....	(f　　　)	分野
expand	....	(f　　　) by ～	その後に～が続く
qualification	....	(v　　　)	さまざまな
participant	....	(r　　　) to ～	
make good use of ～	....		～に関係する
		(a　　　)	意識、知ること
		(e　　　)	存在する

再読編

Training 16 《第3問B形式》

You are talking about a story in a class. 68

Real and Virtual Experience 69

John Horton

When I was a college student, I did a lot of traveling abroad. That was because a professor encouraged me to do so. She said, "Now is the time for you to travel around the world, expand your knowledge through actual experiences and have fun!" I agreed with her.

Since I started to work for a food company, however, I have done most of my traveling via the Internet. By using the Internet, I have seen the sights of many cities on my computer screen. With the help of the Internet, I have also got information about food in different countries. 70

In this way, (A)I was beginning to feel that actual trips were no longer necessary, when I happened to read a famous chef's comment on the Internet. He said, "It is very difficult to have real Italian food in a foreign country, because we eat food and the air around us at the same time. So why don't you fly over to Italy and enjoy real Italian dishes?" 71

Those words reminded me of (B)my professor's advice. As information technology advances, you might be able to do without making some real trips. But (C)this also means that you will miss the various pleasures you can get from traveling. 72

Today there are people who avoid direct contact with others and spend much of their time on the Internet. It is not surprising to see a group of people talking not with each other but into their cellular phone. It seems as if such people are surrounded by an invisible wall. They seem to be losing out on a good chance to meet and talk with other people. 73

I do not think that they are taking good advantage of information technology. We should use information technology as a tool to make our daily communication more fruitful. However, we should never let it reduce our time for face-to-face communication. Let's make use of information technology more wisely, and have great fun in experiencing the actual world. 74

◇本書設問解答欄 1 ____ 2 ____ 3 ____ 4 ____ 5 ____ 6 ____

1. 下線部（A）を和訳しなさい。

____

____

2. 下線部（B）の具体的な内容を日本語で説明しなさい。

____

____

3. 下線部（C）が指す内容を日本語で説明しなさい。

____

____

4. インターネットなどの「仮想世界」の対を成す、筆者が重要だと思っているものを本文から抜き出しなさい。

____

重要語句　（答えは解答解説書「語句」欄の赤字を参照）

encourage	......	(e　　)	経験
expand	......	(k　　)	知識
actual	......	(a　　)	進歩する
agree with ～	......	(s　　)	～を囲む
via	......	(t　　)(a　　) of ～	～を活用する
in this way	......		
remind O of ～	......	(f　　)	実り豊かな
pleasure	......	(r　　)	～を減らす
make use of ～	......	(i　　) of ～	～の代わりに、～をすることなく
recall	......		
		(l　　)	限界
		(c　　)	～を引き起こす

Training 17 《第 4 問形式》

Your teacher is telling your class about students who studied abroad, and your class is going to give their opinions. The first to present is Sarah. 75

Teacher: Study-abroad programs have become increasingly popular among American students. (A)Since the 1980s, many American universities have expanded their study-abroad programs, aiming to increase the number of students who take part in them. The number of American students studying overseas increased slowly at first. Then, in the first decade of the 21st century, it rose by nearly 80%. Europe was the most popular destination, followed by Latin America and Asia. A study was carried out to identify the factors which influenced students' decisions to study abroad. 76

(B)The study involved 231 university students who had studied abroad. They responded to an online survey, which consisted of questions related to the organization of the programs (Program-related Factors) and about students' anticipated experiences while overseas (Experience-related Factors). 77

Table 1 shows the top five Program-related Factors affecting the decisions to study abroad, and the percentages of the participants who placed importance on those factors. The impact that studying abroad would have on the participants' career prospects topped the list. Next, the participants showed concern over whether the study-abroad programs would affect the time when they graduated. This was followed by consideration of how long they would spend abroad. As for the other factors, slightly greater importance was placed on the costs of the programs than on the academic assistance they would receive while abroad. 78

Table 1 *Top Five Program-related Factors*

Factor	Percentage of participants choosing important
Impact on career prospects	91%
(A)	84%
(B)	80%
(C)	74%
(D)	71%

The researchers also examined Experience-related Factors. As Table 2 shows, and as has been seen in other earlier studies, the three leading factors were related to culture, independence, and travel opportunities. Learning how to communicate with people from other cultures and visiting historical sites were also regarded as major factors. The authors of this study had expected that opportunities to learn foreign languages would strongly influence the students' decisions to study abroad. However, less than 40% of the participants mentioned this as a factor. 79

◇本書設問解答欄 1 ____ 2 ____ 3 ____ 4 ____

Table 2 *Top Five Experience-related Factors*

Factor	Percentage of participants choosing important
Learning about other cultures	96%
Learning to be independent	94%
Opportunities to travel	92%
Improving communication skills	88%
Access to historical sites	78%

80 **Sarah:** There are increasing demands in the business world for employees who have studied overseas. Therefore, (C)the findings of this study are useful for universities seeking to improve their students' employment prospects. Likewise, there would be benefits in investigating how the experience of studying abroad influenced what the participants did after returning home.

1. 下線部（A）を和訳しなさい。

____

____

2. 下線部（B）が行われた目的を日本語で答えなさい。

____

____

3. 下線部（C）のように言える理由を日本語で答えなさい。

____

____

重要語句　　（答えは解答解説書「語句」欄の赤字を参照）

expand	....	(d　　　)	目的地、行き先
aim to *do*	....	(c　　　) of ～	～から成る
take part in ～	....	(r　　　) to ～	～に関係している
followed by ～	....	(a　　　)	～を期待して待つ
carry out	....	(c　　　)	懸念、心配
identify	....	(r　　　) ～ as ...	～を…と見なす
prospect	....	(d　　　)	需要
as for ～	....	(e　　　)	雇用、仕事
reduction	....	(i　　　)	～を調べる
expense	....	(s　　　)	安定した

Training 18 《第 5 問形式》

You read a story and made notes about it. 81

In 1949, my parents made the big move from Elmira, New York to Colorado, along with three very tiny children and all their household possessions. My mother had carefully wrapped and packed many precious family treasures, including four boxes of her mother's hand-painted dinner set. Grandmother had painted this lovely set herself, with a pattern of forget-me-not flowers. 82

Unfortunately, something happened during the move. One box of the dinner set didn't make it. It never arrived at our new house, so my mother had only three-quarters of the set: she had plates of different sizes and some serving pieces, but the tea cups and the soup bowls were missing. Often at family gatherings or when we would all sit down for a Thanksgiving or Christmas dinner, (A)my mother would say something about the missing pieces and how she wished they had survived the trip. 83

When my mother died in 1983, I inherited Grandmother's dinner set. I, too, used the set on many special occasions, and I, too, wondered what had happened to the box, never expecting to see the missing pieces again. 84

I love to walk around antique shops and outdoor markets, hunting for treasures. It's great fun to walk up and down early in the morning, watching as the sellers spread their goods on the ground.

(B)I hadn't been to an outdoor market in over a year, until one Sunday in 1993, for some reason I wanted to go. I crawled out of bed at 5 A.M. and drove an hour in the early morning darkness to the giant outdoor market in the suburbs. I walked up and down, and after a couple of hours I was thinking about leaving. I turned the last corner and took a few steps down the row, when I noticed some dishes scattered on the ground. I saw that they were hand-painted with forget-me-nots! I raced over to look at them more closely and carefully picked up a cup and a bowl... forget-me-nots! Exactly like Grandmother's dinner set, with the same delicate strokes and the same thin gold bands around the edges. I looked at the rest of the items — there were the cups! The bowls! They really were Grandmother's! 85

The dealer had noticed my excitement, and when she came over, I told her the story of the missing box. (C1)She said the cups and bowls had come from an estate sale in Lakewood — the next town over from where we had lived when I was a child. She had questioned the owners about the cups and bowls and they said that they had found them in a box in a closet. (C2)They had been (C3)there "forever." 86

I left the market that day, loaded with my amazing treasure. Even now, six years later, I am filled with wonder that (D)so many things came together to let me find 87

◇本書設問解答欄 1 ____ 2 ____ 3 ____ 4 ____ 5 ____

the missing pieces. What would have happened if I had woken later? What gave me the idea to go to the market on that particular day? What if I hadn't turned that last corner, choosing instead to leave and rest my sore feet?

Last week I had a party for some friends. I proudly served soup in those beautiful bowls that had been missing for so long.

1. 下線部（A）を和訳しなさい。

____

____

2. 下線部（B）を和訳しなさい。

____

____

3. 下線部（C1）（C2）（C3）はそれぞれ誰を、あるいは何を指すか。文中の英語で答えなさい。

（C1）______________________________

（C2）______________________________

（C3）______________________________

4. 下線部（D）の意味として最も適切なものを１つ選びなさい。

① 多くの出来事が重なって、行方不明だったディナーセットを野外マーケットで見つけることができた。

② 多くの品物が一同に集められている野外マーケットゆえに、行方が知れなかったディナーセットを発見できた。

③ 野外マーケットで買った多くの品物と一緒に、ずっと探していたディナーセットも見つかった。

④ 野外マーケットで見つけた多くのカップやボウルのおかげで、ディナーセットの欠落を補うことができた。

重要語句　　（答えは解答解説書「語句」欄の赤字を参照）

precious	…………	(i　　　)	～を相続する
make it	…………	(r　　　)	並び、通り
three-quarters	…………	(s　　　)	～をまき散らす
suburb	…………	(r　　　)	急いで行く
delicate	…………	(d　　　)	～を装飾する、塗る

Training 19 《第6問A形式》

You found the following article in a science magazine and made notes about it. 88

While engineers in most of the world try to make robots that perform specific 89 and usually unpleasant tasks, Japanese engineers are always trying to make machines more human. Japan has been the leader of the industrial robot market for the past two decades, and engineers are now working on a new generation of robots that will serve as friends, pets, and social workers. Their goal is to create an intelligent environment in which robots and humans can interact in everyday life.

There are still technical issues that hamper the manufacture of robots that are 90 easy to live with – everything from understanding speech and gestures to making eye contact and having an awareness of human behavior. It will take more time to solve all of these issues, but the first such robots are already starting to appear. For example, guests at the World Expo in Shanghai, China were welcomed by robots that were able to show the guests their way. One company presented a dancing robot. **(A)**<u>Although these robots were a big improvement over robots of the past, they are still just the beginning of what is possible.</u>

However, getting robots to understand real-life human speech may be the hardest 91 job. (**B1**), separating spoken words from background noises and understanding language at the same time has proved to be a big problem. For this reason, scientists are trying to give robots the ability — other than just understanding individual words — to understand the whole of what people are telling them. One new technology is intended to help robots understand the relationships among humans. (**B2**), robots could be programmed to note how long people spend with each other in a room and to take into account friendships among people when communicating with them. Understanding the variety of gestures and signs that people use would help, too.

Robots could get information from the Internet, portable computers, or even 92 television. They might gather additional data from microphones or sensors, noting where someone likes to eat, or what he or she is interested in. Wireless identification (ID) tags are another potential source of information which would allow robots to identify people and acquire information about them. This idea was tested at an elementary school in which students who had been equipped with ID tags were surprised when the robots greeted them by name.

The emphasis on the future function of robots as companions and helpers seems 93 to be deeply Japanese. The reason may have much to do with Japanese popular culture, where robots, like the cartoon cat Doraemon, tend to be portrayed as helpful and friendly. In fact, the tendency to regard lifelike machines as unthreatening may

◇本書解答欄 1 ＿＿ 2 ＿＿ 3 ＿＿ 4 ＿＿

have deeper roots in Japan's Shinto culture, where objects ranging from teapots to samurai swords can have souls. The Japanese government is already promoting projects that have social applications, like nursing or childcare. (C)This may well give a push to the development of more human-like robots because if robots are doing social work, they will have to look and act much more like people than they do now.

1. 下線部（A）を和訳しなさい。

＿＿＿＿＿＿＿＿＿＿＿＿＿＿＿＿＿＿＿＿＿＿＿＿＿＿＿＿＿＿

＿＿＿＿＿＿＿＿＿＿＿＿＿＿＿＿＿＿＿＿＿＿＿＿＿＿＿＿＿＿

2. 文脈から判断して、（B1）（B2）に入る適切なものを、それぞれ 1 つずつ選びなさい。

(B1) ① More importantly ② More specifically
③ Roughly speaking ④ Simply put

(B2) ① Above all ② For example
③ Moreover ④ On the contrary

3. 第 4 段落に関し、ロボットが情報を得る情報源としてはどんなものがあるか。可能性があるものも含めて、挙げられているものをすべて英語のまま抜き出しなさい。

＿＿＿＿＿＿＿＿＿＿＿＿＿＿＿＿＿＿＿＿＿＿＿＿＿＿＿＿＿＿

4. 下線部（C）を和訳しなさい。

＿＿＿＿＿＿＿＿＿＿＿＿＿＿＿＿＿＿＿＿＿＿＿＿＿＿＿＿＿＿

＿＿＿＿＿＿＿＿＿＿＿＿＿＿＿＿＿＿＿＿＿＿＿＿＿＿＿＿＿＿

重 要 語 句　（答えは解答解説書「語句」欄の赤字を参照）

interact	
manufacture	
prove (to be) A	
acquire	
function	
overcome	
laboratory	
(s　　　)	特定の
(s　　　)	具体的に

(i　　　)	個々の
(e　　　) A (　　　) B	A に B を備え付ける
(e　　　) on ～	～を重視すること
(t　　　)	傾向
(r　　　) A as B	A を B と見なす
(p　　　)	～を促進する
(r　　　) to ～	～に反応する

Training 20 《第 6 問 B 形式》

Your group is preparing a poster presentation entitled "The Use of Fire and Human History" using information from the magazine article below. 94

(A)Of all the natural elements, fire seems to fascinate people like no other, and legends and myths about fire can be found in most cultures. For instance, a famous Greek myth from ancient times tells of how fire was stolen from the gods in heaven and brought to earth. Going even further back in time, pieces of fire-hardened cooking pots and burnt bones have been found in East Africa that date back at least one hundred thousand years. 95

The earliest humans did not know how to start a fire, so it is likely that they obtained it through natural events, such as fires caused by lightning, or from forest fires. Desperate to save this fire, our ancestors might have tried to preserve it by setting fire to pieces of wood and then trying to keep them burning continuously. However, (B)this would not have been effective because early humans rarely stayed in one place for very long, and any fires they had been using would go out when they moved from one location to another. Then, probably by chance, one of our early ancestors discovered that sparks are produced when stones are hit against each other, and the making of fire was revolutionized. 96

The lives of early humans changed forever from the moment the first person discovered how to make fire. They found it could be used to provide warmth against cold, light in darkness, and protection against enemies great and small. It could also be used to prepare and preserve the meat from animals they had caught, to harden clay into pots, to shape metals into tools, to clear land for planting, and to hollow logs to make buildings. Indeed, it is difficult to imagine what life today would be like if humans had not mastered the use of fire. 97

History shows that although fire is incredibly useful, it can also be destructive, and (C)there are stories from all parts of the ancient world of whole communities being destroyed by fire. Later, by the beginning of the Middle Ages, towns began to appear in Europe with large buildings constructed of wood. People at this time were worried about the danger of unattended fires, so many towns and villages adopted the practice of reminding their citizens to cover their fires at night. The English king, Alfred, was so worried about fire safety that he passed a law in 876 requiring all fires in the city of Oxford to be covered every day on the ringing of a church bell at 7 p.m. In 1068, King William extended this law, called the curfew law, to the whole of England, but he also prohibited people from gathering outside their homes after dark. This law was very unpopular because it was clearly intended to (**D1**) people's movements, rather than to (**D2**) fires. The curfew law was repealed by King Henry I in 1100, 98

◇本書設問解答欄 1 ____ 2 ____ 3 ____ 4 ____ 5 ____ 6 ____ 7 ____

but the ringing of "curfew bells," as they became known, continued in some churches for more than seven hundred years.

99 Who the first fire user was is a secret lost to history. But, whoever it was, the mastery of fire has shaped our lives more, perhaps, than any other discovery in human history.

1. 下線部（A）をほぼ同じ意味になるように次のように書き換えたとき、（ア）、（イ）それぞれに入る1語を書きなさい。

= ア(　　　　　) seems that no other natural element fascinates people イ(　　　　　) than fire

2. 下線部（B）の指す内容を日本語で答えなさい。

____

____

3. 下線部（C）を和訳しなさい。

____

____

4. （D1）、（D2）に入る語の組み合わせとして最も適切なものを1つ選びなさい。

① (D1) control – (D2) prevent　② (D1) increase – (D2) cause
③ (D1) limit – (D2) save　④ (D1) prohibit – (D2) build

重要語句　（答えは解答解説書「語句」欄の赤字を参照）

legend	…………	**(f**	**)** 〜を魅了する
myth	…………	***be* (d**	**) to *do***
for instance	…………		〜しようと必死になる
ancestor	…………	**(p**	**)** 〜を保存する
by chance	…………	**(r**	**)** ほとんど〜ない
produce	…………	**(c**	**)** 〜を建設する
enemy	…………	**(p**	**)** 慣行
incredibly	…………	**(e**	**)** 〜を広げる
destructive	…………	**(i**	**) O to *do***
adopt	…………		Oが〜することを意図する
remind O to *do*	…………	**(i**	**)** 影響
citizen	…………		

MEMO

MEMO

MEMO

MEMO

共通テスト英語　読解トレーニング ver.2
ナビブック

株式会社エミル出版
〒 102-0072
東京都千代田区飯田橋 2-8-1
Tel ：03-6272-5481
Fax : 03-6272-5482

2020 / 8 / 20 – 初版発行
2023 / 3 / 3 – 改訂版発行

検印欄

1	2	3	4	5
6	7	8	9	10
11	12	13	14	15
16	17	18	19	20

年　　　組　　　番　氏名